Stability of Nonlinear Control Systems

MATHEMATICS IN SCIENCE AND ENGINEERING

A Series of Monographs and Textbooks

Edited by

Richard Bellman

The RAND Corporation, Santa Monica, California

In preparation

STABILITY
OF NONLINEAR
CONTROL SYSTEMS

Solomon Lefschetz

PRINCETON UNIVERSITY
THE NATIONAL UNIVERSITY OF MEXICO
THE RESEARCH INSTITUTE FOR ADVANCED
    STUDIES (RIAS), BALTIMORE, MARYLAND

1965

ACADEMIC PRESS · New York · London

ACADEMIC PRESS INC.
111 Fifth Avenue, New York, New York 10003

United Kingdom Edition published by
ACADEMIC PRESS INC. (LONDON) LTD.
Berkeley Square House, London W.1

LIBRARY OF CONGRESS CATALOG CARD NUMBER: 64-24661

PRINTED IN THE UNITED STATES OF AMERICA

PREFACE

The object of this monograph is to present a concise picture of control stability as it has developed from the direct method of Liapunov. The main impetus for this theory came some fifteen years ago from the work of the Soviet mathematician, A. Lurie, and for a decade or so remained practically a Soviet monopoly. Recently however this monopoly has been broken mainly through the work of V. M. Popov of Romania and of Kalman, LaSalle, and the author in this country.

New developments in the stability of control are so rapid that interesting results are being attained even as this volume goes to press. Although it is impossible, for this reason, to be completely up to date, it is hoped that the interested scientist, mathematician, physicist, or engineer will be able through reading this work to navigate by himself the turbulent waters of nonlinear control theory. It is hoped even more that the engineering "controllist" will find here fruitful material for his operations.

The outline of the monograph is as follows: The first chapter dealing exclusively with the dimensions one and two is quite elementary, and above all does not appeal to vector-matrix technique. Nevertheless, many of the important concepts already make their appearance in this early chapter. However, readers with a fair grasp of linear algebra may pass directly to the next chapters. These chapters, II to VI, present the theory in what may be referred to as the pre-Popov period. Here we lean heavily upon vectors and matrices, except in Chapter VI in which the emphasis is on the discontinuous characteristic. Popov's striking contribution is dealt with in Chapter VII, which is decidedly arduous owing to Popov's extensive use of Fourier transforms and rather advanced analysis. The last control chapter—Chapter VIII—deals primarily with a theorem weaker than Kalman's completion of Popov's second theorem. Our theorem rests upon an important lemma due to Yacubovich. However, in its proof we follow from afar Kalman's noteworthy treatment.

The last chapter consists virtually of a few appendices with which it did not seem appropriate to interrupt the main text.

The author wishes to express his thanks to Dr. Robert Gambill who read most of the manuscript and made numerous corrections and valuable

v

suggestions. He feels that he owes a good deal to discussions with various RIAS colleagues, notably Dr. Kalman, Dr. LaSalle, and Mr. Kenneth Meyer.

The fact that this is the author's second monograph to appear in the Bellman Series is a strong indication of his high regard both for the Series and for the excellent work of the Academic Press.

Finally the author takes pleasure in recognizing his debt to the U.S. Air Force, Office of Scientific Research [Contract AF 49(6δ8)-1242], the U.S. Army Ordnance Missile Command (Contract DA-36-034-ORD-3514 Z), and the National Aeronautics and Space Administration (Contract NASw-718) whose support of our research stimulated this monograph.

Cross references are to the Bibliography at the end, or to chapters in the monograph. Thus (III, 2) or (III, §2) refers to §2 of Chapter III, (III, 2.4) to a statement or a relation 2.4 of §2 in Chapter III; LaSalle [2] refers to item 2 under LaSalle in the Bibliography.

November, 1964   SOLOMON LEFSCHETZ

Special Abridged Notations

n.a.s.c.: Necessary and sufficient conditions

$\quad$ E: Unit matrix

$\qquad$ If A is a square matrix $A_z = zE - A$, so that $|A_z| = 0$ is the characteristic equation of A

$\quad$ c.c.: Completely controllable, complete controllability

$\quad$ c.o.: Completely observable, complete observability

$\quad$ $f * g$: Convolution of the functions f, g

$\varphi(\sigma) = $ characteristic function

$$\Phi(\sigma) = \int_0^\sigma (\sigma)\, d\sigma$$

CONTENTS

Chapter One. Introductory Treatment of Dimensions One and Two

Chapter Two. Indirect Controls

Chapter Three. Indirect Controls (Continued)

Chapter Four. Direct Controls. Linearization Multiple Feedback

Chapter Five. Systems Represented by a Set of Equations of Higher Order

Chapter Six. Discontinuous Characteristics

Chapter Seven. Some Recent Results of V. M. Popov

Chapter Eight. Some Further Recent Contributions

CONTENTS

Chapter Nine.   Miscellaneous Complements

INTRODUCTION

In the present monograph our concern will be solely with socalled real *dynamical systems*; that is, with systems governed by a finite number of real parameters and whose performance is described by a finite set of ordinary differential equations. In order to present a full and clear picture, we propose to describe briefly in this Introduction the various simplifications which experience or practical considerations have imposed.

Let $x_1, x_2, ..., x_n$ be the parameters or coordinates and t the time. Time derivatives are written $\dot{x}, \ddot{x}, ...$. The equations of the system are then of the form

$$(1) \qquad f_h(x_1, ..., x_n, \dot{x}_1, ..., \ddot{x}_1, ..., t) = 0 \qquad (h = 1, 2, ..., p).$$

As is well known, such a system is equivalent to another system of the general type

$$(2) \qquad f_s(y_1, ..., y_m, \dot{y}_1, ..., \dot{y}_m, t) = 0 \qquad (s = 1, 2, ..., m).$$

Our first assumption is that the system (2) may be solved for the derivatives $\dot{y}_1, ..., \dot{y}_m$, thus giving rise to a new system

$$(3) \qquad \dot{y}_j = F_j(y_1, ..., y_m, t) \qquad j = 1, 2, ..., m.$$

If we consider the y_j and the F_j as components of column vectors y, F, (3) may be given the simple form

$$(4) \qquad \dot{y} = F(y, t).$$

1

Let now $y = \eta(t)$ be a particular solution of the system (4) and suppose that for some reason (e.g. stability) we are interested in the behavior of the solutions of (4) in its vicinity. Often the simplest way is to take as a new coordinate vector the vector difference $z = y - \eta(t)$ and substitute in (4). This yields

$$\dot{z} = \dot{y} - \dot{\eta}(t) = F(y, t) - \dot{\eta}(t) = F(z + \eta(t), t) - \dot{\eta}(t),$$

which is of the form

(5) $$\dot{z} = G(z, t), \qquad G(0, t) = 0,$$

with the origin $z = 0$ corresponding to our earlier special solution $y = \eta(t)$. The origin is a "point-solution" or *critical point* of the new system (5). We are now merely interested in the neighborhood of the origin.

Mainly for reasons of mathematical convenience we shall only consider systems "without t" at the right:

(6) $$\dot{z} = G(z), \qquad G(0) = 0,$$

or *autonomous systems*. Main reason: they are so much more manageable than *nonautonomous systems*.

Let Σ be an autonomous n vector system

(7) $$\dot{x} = X(x).$$

One may be especially interested in what happens to the solutions in the neighborhood of the origin $x = 0$, which we assume to be a critical point: $X(0) = 0$. Suppose also that the system contains a control mechanism aiming to maintain the solutions as close as possible to the solution $x = 0$. Let it be assumed finally that one has been able to divide the components $x_1, ..., x_n$ of x into two sets: the *system components* $y_1, ..., y_p$ and the *control components* $z_1, ..., z_q$, where $p + q = n$. The system components define the state p vector y (describing the state of the system) and the z_h define the control q vector z. The system assumes then the form

(8) (a) $\dot{y} = Y(y, z)$, (b) $\dot{z} = Z(y, z)$,

$$Y(0,0) = 0, \qquad\qquad Z(0, 0) = 0.$$

The system *without control or the fundamental system*, as we shall call it, is

(9) $$\dot{y} = Y(y, 0).$$

2

The purpose of the control mechanism may now be stated as aiming to *secure* or possibly to *improve* the asymptotic stability behavior of the origin, principally as regards the state vector y.

Now in this general form the system is only rarely tractable and so one must have recourse to *partial* or complete *linearization*.

Complete linearization has been applied most extensively in control theory and technique. In substance it replaces the system (8) by linear approximations. Linear equations with constant coefficients are easily dealt with, and under the linearity assumption one may proceed quite far, so this is a well-beaten path only touched upon in Chapter V.

In what follows the system but not the control vector will be linearized. As the fundamental system is generally quite stable, this is reasonable enough. The control, however, may involve a servomotor operating beyond a reasonable linearization of its characteristic. Our scheme will then assume the general form

(10)
$$\dot{y} = Ay + F(z)$$
$$\dot{z} = Cy + G(z).$$

Actually we shall deal almost exclusively with the case where the control variable z is a scalar (one-dimensional) and with the numerous related problems that even this relatively simple case presents. There are two basic types: (a) direct control; (b) indirect control. They may be represented jointly by a vector-matrix system

(11)
$$\dot{x} = Ax - \xi b$$
$$\begin{matrix}(a) & \xi \\ (b) & \dot{\xi}\end{matrix}\Bigg\} = \varphi(\sigma)$$
$$\sigma = c'x - \rho\xi$$

where the designations are the vector designations of (II, §1). The second type is (practically) the more important and receives most of our attention later. From the formal standpoint one may reduce each of these systems to the other.

The system (11) raises the double question of the existence and uniqueness of the paths through any point of the x [the x, ξ] space in direct [indirect] controls. One of the conditions imposed upon $\varphi(\sigma)$ (except in VI) is continuity. A very complete existence theorem (see the beginning of Niemickii and Stepanov [1]) will then guarantee existence but not uniqueness of paths. Most practical functions $\varphi(\sigma)$ have continuous "broken line"

3

graphs, that is, consist of a finite number of arcs with unique and continuously turning tangent at each point. For these one may apply the existence theorem of Lefschetz ([1], p. 31, plus the (hardly modified) complement of p. 34) and pleasantly achieve both existence and path uniqueness. We will not return to these questions in the sequel.

Since our fundamental problem is a stability problem, recourse must be had to the only general stability method available: Liapunov's direct method. A résumé is given in (IX, §4). More complete information will be found in LaSalle and Lefschetz [1].

Observe that uniqueness of path is never required in the Liapunov theory.

A word of caution. The linearization of both the system and the control has brought about a certain special, almost algebraic technique in control theory. This technique had best be abandoned when one comes to nonlinear controls, and the differential equations faced directly, so that one sees clearly what mathematical theories (mainly due to Liapunov) must be applied. It is no small merit indeed of the Soviet leaders to have consistently done so from the beginning.

Historical remark. Indirect controls, of such importance in modern industry, were first introduced some forty years ago by N. Minorsky [1] under the name of *derivative control* in connection with the control of ship motions (research carried out for the U.S. Navy). The modern impetus in the study of this general type of control was given by Lurie of Leningrad.

Chapter 1

INTRODUCTORY TREATMENT OF DIMENSIONS ONE AND TWO

It so happens that a number of the major ideas and problems to be faced more fully later already appear for dimensions one and two. By way of introducing the general topic it seems worthwhile to deal at first somewhat fully with these elementary cases. This is the aim of the present chapter. For simplicity all quantities considered here will be scalars. In the later chapters the vector-matrix notation will be adopted in full force.

§1. The Characteristic Function

The nonlinearity to be faced throughout the sequel will be caused by the *characteristic function* $\varphi(\sigma)$ of the control mechanism. Here σ is the so-called *feedback signal*, and the nonlinearity comes, usually, from a servomechanism or more generally from the nature of the control mechanism. From the standpoint of our mathematical treatment, what matters is the nature of the function $\varphi(\sigma)$, and since this will appear in every system under consideration we may as well deal with it here and now.

Characteristic functions may be very varied indeed. Some frequent types are given in Fig. 1. The first two are continuous; the other two are discontinuous. The discontinuous types present serious difficulties which will be discussed in (VI, §1). Except for these we shall limit the functions $\varphi(\sigma)$ to a class said to be *admissible* governed by the following:

Assumptions regarding characteristics.

I. The function $\varphi(\sigma)$ is defined and continuous for all values of σ.

II. $\varphi(\sigma) = 0$, $\sigma\varphi(\sigma) > 0$ for all $\sigma \neq 0$, i.e., $\varphi(\sigma)$ has the sign of σ.

III. The integrals

$$\int_0^{\pm\infty} \varphi(\sigma)\,d\sigma \quad \text{diverge.}$$

The first property states in substance that the graph of $\varphi(\sigma)$ has no jumps; the second property states that the graph is situated in the first and third quadrants; finally according to the third property the area under the graph tends to infinity at both ends.

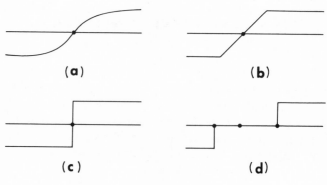

(a)

(b)

(c)

(d)

FIG. 1

As a matter of fact it will be shown in (III, §4) that property III may usually be dispensed with.

The function $\Phi(\sigma)$. This function, of constant occurrence later, is defined as

$$\Phi(\sigma) = \int_0^\sigma \varphi(\sigma)\,d\sigma.$$

It is continuous, zero for $\sigma = 0$, positive otherwise as a consequence of II, and $\to \infty$ as $\sigma \to \pm\infty$ as follows from III.

6

§2. Systems of Dimension Unity. Direct Control

Consider a system depending upon a single real variable. As described in the Introduction, one may select this variable, e.g., x, so that the desired position to be controlled corresponds to the value $x = 0$. Thus x represents the deviation that it is desired to minimize. Let the fundamental system be represented by a linear equation

$$(2.1) \qquad \dot{x} = kx,$$

where k is a constant $\neq 0$. The purpose of the control would be to accentuate the "return to zero" of the variable x.

There are now essentially two distinct possibilities according to the manner of operating of the feedback. In a *direct control* it operates directly upon the system, in an *indirect control* it operates through one or more derivatives. In the former the operation is apt to be rather hard, through a ponderous mechanism. In an indirect control on the other hand, by making use of derivatives one may operate through a comparatively light scheme. For this reason indirect controls are often preferred to the other kind. At all events, mathematically, they are also much more interesting and for this reason they have been studied more extensively.

In the present section we first deal with direct control. Physically speaking, a direct control regulating the system (2.1) is described by a system

$$(2.2) \qquad \dot{x} = kx + \xi, \qquad \xi = \varphi(\sigma), \qquad \sigma = cx, \qquad c \neq 0.$$

This system is equivalent to the single equation

$$(2.3) \qquad \dot{x} = kx + \varphi(cx)$$

which is formally as simple as could be desired. It may actually be integrated as

$$(2.4) \qquad \int_{x_0}^{x} \frac{dx}{kx + \varphi(cx)} = t - t_0.$$

If one knows *exactly* the characteristic φ, one may calculate the solution. In practice this is not as interesting as it may seem. For various reasons the characteristic is often variable within a certain range, and it becomes important to estimate the effect of the control under these special circumstances, and perhaps to impose upon its parameters conditions guaranteeing suitable stability.

7

Now in the present instance one may readily find suitable restrictions guaranteeing the return of the system to zero no matter what its initial position. For the velocity at any time is $kx + \varphi(cx)$. It is thus sufficient that this quantity have the sign of $-x$, i.e. that

$$f(x) = -kx^2 - x\varphi(cx) = -kx^2 - \frac{1}{c}(cx)\varphi(cx) > 0.$$

There are now two possibilities;

(a) $k < 0$. That is the basic system is already stable. To increase this feature one merely needs to increase $f(x)$ for all x. Since $u\varphi(u) > 0$, and $-kx^2 > 0$ it is sufficient to choose the parameter c negative.

(b) $k > 0$. To have $f(x) > 0$, one must first select c negative and also such that the graph of $\varphi(-cx)$ passes below the line $y = kx$ when $x < 0$ and above it when $x > 0$. By this means the control will change the unstable system (2.1) into a stable system: all solutions $\to 0$ as $t \to \infty$.

§3. System of Dimension Unity. Indirect Control

The system just treated could hardly be more elementary. Indirect controls of one dimensional systems however present many of the features and complications of higher dimensional systems.

We begin by choosing as fundamental system

(3.1) $$\dot{x} = -kx, \qquad k > 0,$$

so that the initial system is already stable. The effect of the control is to replace the system of order one (3.1) by a new system of order two,

(3.2)
$$\dot{x} = -kx - b\xi$$
$$\dot{\xi} = \varphi(\sigma)$$
$$\sigma = cx - \rho\xi,$$

where the constants b, c, ρ are the *control parameters*. It is evident that one must have $b \neq 0$, since $b = 0$ means that the control has no effect upon the system. But then one may replace the coordinate x by a new coordinate $x^* = x/b$. This is merely a change of scale for x. The new system assumes the form

$$x^* = -kx^* + \xi$$
$$\dot{\xi} = \varphi(\sigma)$$
$$\sigma = bcx^* - \rho\xi.$$

Upon writing now x for x^* and c for bc we have the system

$$\dot{x} = -kx + \xi$$

(3.3)
$$\dot{\xi} = \varphi(\sigma)$$

$$\sigma = cx - \rho\xi,$$

which is like (3.2) but with $b = -1$. The control parameters are now c, ρ.

Regarding the existence and uniqueness of solutions see the end of the Introduction.

The fundamental system (3.1) is already asymptotically stable and one wishes to strengthen this properly. In fact, one would like to solve:

Lurie's problem. To find n.a.s.c. for the asymptotic stability of the system (3.3) regardless of the initial conditions and whatever the choice of admissible characteristic function $\varphi(\sigma)$. That is, one would like to have n.a.s.c. to guarantee that any solution $(x(t), \xi(t))$, of (3.3) tends to the origin $(0, 0)$ regardless of the choice of $\varphi(\sigma)$. This is known as *absolute stability*.

Observe that technically speaking, to solve this problem is actually more than one needs, for the variables x, ξ will be limited in extent and it would be sufficient to demand that all the solutions emanating from some bounded region R of the (x, ξ) plane do tend to the origin regardless of the choice of φ. However, in the absence of definiteness as regards the region R one may as well, and more easily, take R as the whole plane.

In order to discuss absolute stability it is convenient at this stage to choose as coordinate, instead of ξ, the parameter σ which appears in $\varphi(\sigma)$. The best way to achieve this is by means of a linear transformation of coordinates from x, ξ to y, σ defined as follows:

(3.4)
$$y = -kx + \xi, \qquad \sigma = cx - \rho\xi$$

The equations for the (y, σ) system are found at once to be

$$\dot{y} = -ky + \varphi(\sigma)$$

(3.5)
$$\dot{\sigma} = cy - \rho\varphi(\sigma).$$

As regards stability, the system (3.5) will be entirely equivalent to the system (3.3) if, and only if, the transformation (3.4) is nonsingular, that is if (3.4) may be solved uniquely for x, ξ in terms of y, σ. For then the "y, σ picture" will be essentially like the "x, ξ picture"—the x, ξ picture seen at "an angle" as it were. The necessary and sufficient condition (n.a.s.c.) to have this happen is that the determinant of the coefficients of x, ξ in (3.4) be $\neq 0$, or that

$$(3.6) \qquad k\rho - c \neq 0.$$

This is a first restriction on the control parameters ρ, c. It is assumed henceforth and we now deal solely with y, σ and the system (3.5).

Since critical points are solutions, it is clear that a necessary condition for absolute stability is that in the y, σ plane the origin be the only critical point, i.e. the only solution of the system

$$(3.7) \qquad -ky + \varphi(\sigma) = 0, \qquad cy - \rho\varphi(\sigma) = 0.$$

In view of (3.6) the only solution of this system in the unknowns $y, \varphi(\sigma)$ is $y = 0$, $\varphi(\sigma) = 0$. Since $\varphi(\sigma) \neq 0$ for $\sigma \neq 0$, the only solution of (3.7) is $y = \sigma = 0$, and so we are assured that the origin is in effect the only critical point in sight.

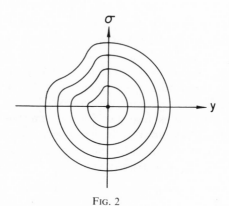

FIG. 2

Our treatment of absolute stability of the system (3.5) rests upon a fundamental result due to Liapunov. While his general theorem (see IX, §4) requires a good deal of technique (owing to its "n-dimensional" feature) it is intuitively accessible in our low dimensional case.

Suppose that in some manner there has been found a continuous infinity of ovals surrounding the origin in the y, σ plane (Fig. 2). If we are in a position to show that every solution of the system (3.5) crosses every oval inward, and this regardless of the choice of the characteristic $\varphi(\sigma)$, our purpose will have been achieved. This is in substance the *geometric formulation* of Liapunov's so-called direct method.

The ovals which we choose, following Lurie and Postnikov (see Lurie [1]), are the curves

(3.8) $$V = py^2 + \Phi(\sigma) = h,$$

where p, h are positive constants. That they are ovals surrounding the origin is established readily enough. The curve C represented by (3.7) may be plotted from the relation

$$y = \pm \sqrt{\frac{h}{p} - \frac{\Phi(\sigma)}{p}}.$$

We must have $\Phi \le h$, which yields $-a \le \sigma \le b$, a and b positive. Hence, the curve has the aspect of Fig. 3. This is an oval symmetric with respect to the σ axis.

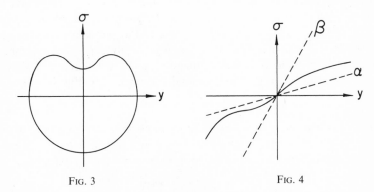

FIG. 3   FIG. 4

The construction of the ovals is only part of the story. Let γ be the path defined by a solution $(y(t), \sigma(t))$ of our system. Along γ the function $V(y(t), \sigma(t)) = V(t)$ must decrease since we desire that γ tend to the origin as $t \to +\infty$. Hence we desire that $\dot{V} < 0$ along every γ, or that

$$-\dot{V}(y(t), \sigma(t)) = -(2py\dot{y} + \varphi(\sigma)\dot{\sigma}) = 2pky^2 + \rho\varphi^2(\sigma) - 2\left(p + \frac{c}{2}\right)\varphi(\sigma)y > 0$$

for all choices of y and $\varphi(\sigma)$. This will happen, since $pk > 0$, provided that both roots of

$$2pku^2 - 2\left(p + \frac{c}{2}\right)u + \rho = 0$$

11

are complex, i.e. if

$$(3.9) \qquad f(p) = \left(p + \frac{c}{2}\right)^2 - 2pk\rho = p^2 + (c - 2\rho k)p + \frac{c^2}{4} < 0.$$

Let p_1, p_2 be the two roots of $f(p) = 0$ and δ its discriminant. We have

$$\delta = (c - 2\rho k)^2 - c^2 = 4\rho k(\rho k - c),$$

$$p_1 + p_2 = 2\rho k - c, \qquad p_1 p_2 = \frac{c^2}{4}.$$

Now (3.9) requires that the roots of $f(p) = 0$ be real and distinct and that $p_1 < p < p_2$. The roots will be real and distinct if, and only if, $\delta > 0$, or $\rho k > c$.

Since one must be able to choose $p > 0$, one must have $p_2 > 0$. Since $p_1 p_2 > 0$, both roots have the same sign and this sign is that of $p_1 + p_2$. Hence we must have $\rho k > c/2$, which holds if $\rho k > c$. Thus this last condition which is just (3.6) is sufficient to guarantee absolute stability.

In the case just discussed, there is a certain unreality, for owing to $k > 0$, the fundamental system is already largely asymptotically stable. The effect of the control is then to make it more so. A more natural situation takes place when the fundamental system is actually unstable:

$$\dot{x} = kx, \qquad k > 0,$$

and the effect of the control must be to make the system stable. This will occur only with a characteristic of a certain special type. To simplify matters, assume that for $|\sigma|$ small $\varphi(\sigma)$ has a power series expansion

$$\varphi(\sigma) = g\sigma + \psi(\sigma)$$

where g is a positive constant, and ψ begins with terms of degree at least two, and otherwise has the properties II, III earlier imposed on φ. As φ is not precisely fixed, we assume that g may vary within certain limits: $0 < \alpha \leqq g \leqq \beta$. Notice that in substance, the graph of φ is now a curve with positive slope g through the origin, and that this slope may vary between α and β (Fig. 4). The equations with control are thus

$$\dot{y} = ky + g\sigma + \psi(\sigma)$$

$$\dot{\sigma} = cy - \rho g\sigma - \rho\psi(\sigma).$$

For $|\sigma|$ sufficiently small, one may achieve asymptotic stability if the roots r_1, r_2 of the equation

12

$$\begin{vmatrix} k - r & g \\ c & -g\rho - r \end{vmatrix} = r^2 + (g\rho - k)r - gc - \rho g k = 0$$

have negative real parts. (LaSalle and Lefschetz [1, p. 48].) Now

$$r_1 r_2 = -g(c + \rho k), \qquad r_1 + r_2 = k - \rho g.$$

Whether r_1, r_2 are both real or complex one must have

$$r_1 r_2 > 0, \qquad r_1 + r_2 < 0,$$

i.e.

$$c + \rho k < 0, \qquad k - \rho g < 0,$$

and hence finally

$$\frac{k}{g} < \rho < \frac{-c}{k}.$$

Since $k > 0$ this implies in particular that $c < 0$.

The asymptotic stability obtained is only of local character—only for $|\sigma|$ sufficiently small.

§4. System of Order Two

It is convenient to deal first with indirect controls. Let the fundamental system be

$$(4.1) \qquad \dot{x}_i = -k_i x_i; \qquad i = 1, 2; \qquad k_i > 0,$$

and let the system with control be

$$x_i = -k_i x_i - \xi b_i, \qquad i = 1, 2$$

$$(4.2) \qquad \dot{\xi} = \varphi(\sigma)$$

$$\sigma = c_1 x_1 + c_2 x_2 - \rho \xi$$

where $\varphi(\sigma)$ is an admissible characteristic function.

For existence and uniqueness of the solutions see the end of the Introduction.

13

Since $\varphi(\sigma) = 0$ if and only if $\sigma = 0$, the origin $x_i = 0$, $\xi = 0$ will be the only critical point provided that the determinant

$$\Delta = \begin{vmatrix} -k_1 & 0 & -b_1 \\ 0 & -k_2 & -b_2 \\ c_1 & c_2 & -\rho \end{vmatrix} \neq 0.$$

Upon expanding Δ and dividing by $k_1 k_2 \neq 0$ this condition becomes

(4.3)
$$\rho + \frac{b_1 c_1}{k_1} + \frac{b_2 c_2}{k_2} \neq 0.$$

Assume for the present that it is fulfilled. As in the previous case it is convenient to apply a coordinate transformation from the variables x_1, x_2, ξ to new variables y_1, y_2, σ defined by

(4.4)
$$\begin{aligned} y_1 &= -k_1 x_1 - b_1 \xi \\ y_2 &= -k_2 x_2 - b_2 \xi \\ \sigma &= c_1 x_1 + c_2 x_2 - \rho \xi. \end{aligned}$$

The determinant of the transformation is Δ, and so, under the assumption that (4.3) holds, the transformation is nonsingular. Thus again the stability properties will not be affected by the transformation. The differential equations in the new variables are found at once to be

(4.5)
$$\begin{aligned} \dot{y}_i &= -k_i y_i - b_i \varphi(\sigma), \qquad i = 1, 2 \\ \dot{\sigma} &= c_1 y_1 + c_2 y_2 - \rho \varphi(\sigma). \end{aligned}$$

In imitation of the treatment of the preceding case, consider the surfaces

$$V(y, \sigma) = y_1{}^2 + y_2{}^2 + \Phi(\sigma) = a^2.$$

They represent surfaces of revolution around the σ axis generated by the curves

$$y_1{}^2 + \Phi(\sigma) = a^2.$$

We have seen that these curves are concentric ovals around the origin. Hence our surfaces are likewise concentric ovals (of dimension two) around the origin.

14

§4. SYSTEM OF ORDER TWO

We must find conditions under which the space ovals are all crossed inward by any path γ of (4.5). Along such a path

$$\dot{V}(y, \sigma) = 2y_1(-k_1y_1 - \varphi(\sigma)b_1) + 2y_2(-k_2y_2 - \varphi(\sigma)b_2)$$
$$+ \varphi(\sigma)(c_1y_1 + c_2y_2) - \rho\varphi^2(\sigma) = -2(k_1y_1^2 + k_2y_2^2) - \rho\varphi^2(\sigma)$$
$$- 2d_1y_1\varphi(\sigma) - 2d_2y_2\varphi(\sigma),$$

$$d_i = b_i - \tfrac{1}{2}c_i, \qquad i = 1, 2.$$

The expression $\dot{V}$ is to be negative for all y_1, y_2 and σ not all zero. Since $\varphi(\sigma) = 0$, if and only if, $\sigma = 0$, this is the same as demanding that $-\dot{V}$ be positive for all y_1, y_2 and $\varphi(\sigma)$ not all zero. This is the condition that all the paths penetrate every oval *without exception*. Now

$$(4.6) \qquad -\dot{V} = 2\left\{ k_1\left(y_1 + \frac{d_1}{2k_1} \right)^2 + k_2\left(y_2 + \frac{d_2}{2k_2} \right)^2 \right\}$$

$$+ \left(\rho - \frac{d_1^2}{2k_1} - \frac{d_2^2}{2k_2} \right)\varphi^2(\sigma).$$

A sufficient condition for absolute stability is then

$$(4.7) \qquad \rho > \frac{d_1^2}{2k_1} + \frac{d_2^2}{2k_2}.$$

The right-hand side is positive unless $d_1 = d_2 = 0$. In any case (4.7) implies that $\rho > 0$.

It is interesting to compare the inequalities (4.3) and (4.7). Identically

$$(b - \tfrac{1}{2}c)^2 + 2bc = (b + \tfrac{1}{2}c)^2 \geqq 0.$$

Hence

$$\frac{(b_1 - \tfrac{1}{2}c_1)^2}{2k_1} + \frac{(b_2 - \tfrac{1}{2}c_2)^2}{2k_2} \geqq -\frac{b_1c_1}{k_1} - \frac{b_2c_2}{k_2}.$$

That is the inequality (4.7) implies (4.3). Hence (4.7) *alone is a sufficient condition for absolute stability.*

This result is a special case of an analogous and more general property due to LaSalle and taken up later (III, §4).

15

Direct control. The controlled system is now

(4.8)
$$x_i = -k_i x_i - b_i \varphi(\sigma), \qquad i = 1, 2$$

$$\sigma = c_1 x_1 + c_2 x_2.$$

In the absence of ξ one will not need to change coordinates. However, a difficulty arises regarding the condition that the origin be the only critical point. This requires that the relations

$$-k_i x_i + b_i \varphi(c_1 x_1 + c_2 x_2) = 0, \qquad i = 1, 2$$

have the origin as their unique solution. In the absence of further information as to $\varphi(\sigma)$ we can only assume that this is the case.

Choose again

$$V(x_1, x_2) = x_1{}^2 + x_2{}^2 + \Phi(\sigma).$$

Since $\Phi(\sigma) > 0$ for all $\sigma \neq 0$ and $\Phi(0) = 0$, V is positive for all x_1, x_2 not both zero. From (4.8) there follows

(4.9) $\quad \dot{\sigma} = c_1 \dot{x}_1 + c_2 \dot{x}_2 = -k_1 c_1 x_1 - k_2 c_2 x_2 + (b_1 c_1 + b_2 c_2) \varphi(\sigma).$

By analogy then with the preceding case we find

$$-\dot{V} = 2\left\{ k_1 \left(x_1 + \frac{d_1}{2k_1} \right)^2 + k_2 \left(x_2 + \frac{d_2}{2k_2} \right)^2 \right\}$$

$$+ \left(\rho - \frac{d_1{}^2}{2k_1} - \frac{d_2{}^2}{2k_2} \right) \varphi^2(\sigma)$$

where

$$\rho = (b_1 c_1 + b_2 c_2).$$

However, as shown in (IV, §1) one can only achieve here

(4.10) $\qquad (b_1 c_1 + b_2 c_2) = \dfrac{(b_1 - \frac{1}{2} c_1)^2}{2k_1} + \dfrac{(b_2 - \frac{1}{2} c_2)^2}{2k_2}.$

It will still guarantee absolute stability, but this is as far as we will proceed in this direction.

16

Chapter 2

INDIRECT CONTROLS

With this chapter we initiate the general study of controls for n dimensional systems and it is continued in the next chapters. For the convenience of the reader some notions introduced in the previous chapter will be repeated. For the characteristic $\varphi(\sigma)$ however, we shall depend upon (I, §1).

In dealing with a general dimension, vectors and matrices are obviously advantageous and they are discussed in §1.

§1. Vectors and Matrices

By and large the notations and designations are those of LaSalle and Lefschetz [1, Chapt. I]. As a rule $a, b, c, ..., x, y$ will denote vectors and $A, B, C, ..., X, Y$ will denote matrices, while small Greek letters will stand for scalars. In particular x denotes the column vector, one column matrix, whose components are x_j, and A the matrix (a_{jk}).

The designation E_n, or E when n is obvious, represents the unit-matrix of order n. The transpose of a matrix $A = (a_{ij})$ is the matrix, written A', whose elements are the symmetric of those of A relative to its principal diagonal. In particular the $1 \times n$ matrix x', corresponding to x above, is the one-row matrix: row vector, with the same elements as x.

If $A = (a_{jk})$ is a complex matrix A^* denotes the matrix $(\bar{a}_{kj})$ that is $(\bar{a}_{jk})'$. Abstractly $(\ )^* = (^-)'$. Note that if A is square and nonsingular so that its inverse A^{-1} is defined, the operation of inversion commutes with $(\ )'$ or $(\ )^*$ as the case may be (proof elementary). That is $(A^{-1})' = (A')^{-1}$ or $(A^{-1})^* = (A^*)^{-1}$, for A square and nonsingular; also for any $A : (\bar{A})' = \overline{(A')}$.

Note also the following property. If x, y are both n vectors, then

(1.1)
$$x'y = \sum x_j y_j = y'x.$$

Recall that xy' represents the $n \times n$ matrix

(1.2)
$$xy' = (x_j y_k).$$

The designation $V(x)$ stands for a Liapunov type scalar function of the vector x.

The gradient operator $(\partial/\partial x_1,..., \partial/\partial x_n)$ is thought of as a one-row matrix operator $\partial/\partial x$. Thus $\partial V/\partial x$ represents the row vector with components $\partial V/\partial x_j$.

For easy reference we repeat that an $n \times n$ matrix A, whose characteristic roots all have negative real parts, is said to be *stable*.

If the quadratic form $x'Fx$ or hermitian form x^*Hx are > 0 $[< 0]$ for all $x \neq 0$ we write F or $H > 0[< 0]$.

For further remarks on quadratic or hermitian forms see (IX, §1).

§2. Indirect Control. General Type

Recall that the difference between direct and indirect control is that the operation of the feedback is direct in the first and indirect—through a derivative—in the second. In our treatment indirect controls will serve as the predominant model and so they are fully discussed first.

Let the fundamental (state) system be $\dot{x} = Ax$ where x is an n vector and A a constant $n \times n$ matrix. Let the control depend upon a single coordinate ξ. The indirect control system is (Lurie [1])

(2.1)
$$\dot{x} = Ax - \xi b$$
$$\dot{\xi} = \qquad \varphi(\sigma)$$
$$\sigma = c'x - \rho\xi$$

where b, c are constant n vectors and φ is an admissible characteristic. This time we assume explicitly that A is nonsingular.

For the existence and uniqueness of the solutions see the end of the Introduction.

Lurie's problem. To find n.a.s.c. to have (2.1) asymptotically stable in the large and this for all choices of an admissible $\varphi(\sigma)$. It implies that all solutions $(x(t), \xi(t))$ of (2.1) $\rightarrow 0$: $x = 0$, $\xi = 0$, as $t \rightarrow +\infty$ and this whatever an admissible $\varphi(\sigma)$. This is *absolute stability*.

Owing to the special role of the parameter σ in relation to the system (2.1) it is manifestly desirable to choose coordinates with σ one of them. This is achieved by the transformation (2.2) given below. The important point is that the system in the new coordinates possess the same asymptotic stability properties as the initial system. To that end the only requirement is that the transformation be nonsingular. For it is then readily shown that if, in the initial system, the origin is asymptotically stable for all admissible φ, then the same property holds in the new system (see LaSalle and Lefschetz [1, p. 77]).

Take then the transformation $(x, \xi) \rightarrow (y, \sigma)$ given by

$$(2.2) \qquad y = Ax - b\xi, \qquad \sigma = c'x - \rho\xi,$$

replacing (2.1) by

$$\dot{y} = Ay - b\varphi(\sigma)$$
$$(2.3)$$
$$\dot{\sigma} = c'y - \rho\varphi(\sigma).$$

For n.a.s.c. to have the transformation (2.2) nonsingular is that the determinant

$$(2.4) \qquad \begin{vmatrix} A & -b \\ c' & -\rho \end{vmatrix} \neq 0.$$

Since A is stable $|A| \neq 0$. Hence this relation yields (IX, §2)

$$(2.5) \qquad \rho \neq c'A^{-1}b,$$

and this is assumed henceforth.

Since a critical point is a solution, absolute stability requires that the origin $y = 0$, $\sigma = 0$ be the only critical point of the system (2.3). Since $\varphi(\sigma) = 0$ if and only if $\sigma = 0$, (2.5) expresses also a n.a.s.c. for the origin to be the only critical point of (2.3).

19

Passing now to the problem of absolute stability, a first observation must be made regarding the matrix A itself. The system (2.3) must be asymptotically stable whenever one chooses the admissible function $\varphi = \mu\sigma, \mu > 0$. Hence the matrix of this linear system

$$\begin{pmatrix} A & -\mu b \\ c' & -\mu\rho \end{pmatrix}$$

must have no characteristic roots with positive real parts. Now for μ small, these roots are very near those of A and the root zero. Hence A must have no root with positive real part. Let a matrix whose characteristic roots all have nonpositive real parts be referred to as *critical* or *semistable*. Thus a *first necessary condition for absolute stability is that the matrix A be semistable*.

Since semistability brings about many complications (discussed in IV) *we assume for the present that A is stable*.

Now the only general method available for absolute stability rests upon Liapunov's asymptotic stability theorem (IX, 4.5) plus the Barbashin and Krassovskii complement (IX, 4.7). Following Lurie and Postnikov we look for a Liapunov function of type

(2.6) $$V(y, \sigma) = y'By + \Phi(\sigma),$$

and calculate its time derivative along the paths of (2.3):

$$\dot{V} = \dot{y}'By + yB\dot{y} + \varphi(\sigma)\dot{\sigma}.$$

Hence from (2.3):

(2.7) $$-\dot{V} = y'Cy + \rho\varphi^2(\sigma) + 2\varphi(\sigma)d'y$$

where

(2.8) $$d = Bb - \tfrac{1}{2}c$$

and more importantly we have the Liapunov relation

(2.9) $$A'B + BA = -C.$$

Referring to Liapunov's theorem we must first have $V(y, \sigma)$ positive definite (see IX, §4), for all values of y and σ. This requires that $B > 0$. When this condition is fulfilled we will have $V > 0$ if $y \neq 0$ and also > 0 if $y = 0, \sigma \neq 0$ since then $\Phi > 0$ (property II of I, §1). This will actually hold for all admissible functions $\varphi(\sigma)$. Finally since $B > 0$ the expression $|y'By| \to \infty$ with $\|y\|$, and owing to property III of (I, §1) $\Phi(\sigma) \to \infty$ with

$\|y\| + |\sigma|$. Thus the requirement of the Barbashin and Krassovskii complement is actually fulfilled. That is the requirements on $V(y, \sigma)$ for absolute stability are satisfied through the mere fact that $B > 0$.

There remains then to arrange matters so that $- \dot{V}$ is positive definite for all y, σ. Here we have the fortunate circumstance that $- \dot{V}$ contains σ only through $\varphi(\sigma)$, and is a quadratic form in y and φ. (This is the great merit of the Lurie and Postnikov type of function V.) It suffices therefore to demand that $- \dot{V}$ be a positive definite quadratic form in y and φ. The n.a.s.c. due to Sylvester, is that the principal minors of the matrix

$$\begin{pmatrix} C & d \\ d' & \rho \end{pmatrix}$$

all be positive. In particular this must hold for C and so $C > 0$, hence $|C| \neq 0$. Beyond this we still require that the determinant

$$\begin{vmatrix} C & d \\ d' & \rho \end{vmatrix} > 0.$$

Referring then to (IX, §2) this yields the *fundamental inequality*

(F$_i$) $\qquad\qquad\qquad\qquad \rho > d'C^{-1}d.$

Notice incidentally that it implies that

(2.10) $\qquad\qquad\qquad\qquad \rho > 0,$

an inequality obvious enough since it merely states that $- \dot{V}(0, \sigma) > 0$.

Since $C > 0$ implies $B > 0$, the only conditions left are $C > 0$ and (F$_i$). Hence

(2.11) **Theorem.** *N.a.s.c. in order that the Liapunov function $V(y, \sigma)$ of (2.6) be positive definite for all y, σ, and that $- \dot{V} = - \dot{V}(y(t), \sigma(t))$ along the solutions of (2.3) be a positive definite quadratic form in y and φ (hence positive definite in y, σ) are $C > 0$ and (F$_i$).*

When these conditions are fulfilled the system (2.3) (hence also (2.1)) is absolutely stable.

PROOF OF NECESSITY. Since $- \dot{V}$ is a positive definite quadratic form in (y, φ) we must have $C > 0$ and (F$_i$).

PROOF OF SUFFICIENCY. If $C > 0$ and (F$_i$) hold $- \dot{V}$ is a positive definite quadratic form in (y, φ). From $C > 0$ follows then by Liapunov's relation $B > 0$, and hence by our earlier argument that V is positive definite for all y, σ and all admissible functions $\varphi(\sigma)$.

21

(2.12) *Properties $C > 0$ and* (F_i) *imply* (2.5).

They imply absolute stability and hence that the origin is the only critical point, from which (2.5) follows.

Another proof (algebraic) of (2.12) will be given in the next chapter (III, 2.2).

The preceding scheme will guide us throughout the sequel and we formulate:

General rule. *In seeking absolute stability we will usually look for a Liapunov function $V(y, \sigma)$ positive definite in (y, σ) such that $-\dot{V}$ is a positive definite quadratic form in (y, φ).*

Of course any other state variable, for example x, could replace y.

§3. Comparison with a Recent Result of Yacubovich

The inequality (F_i) may be phrased as follows:

(3.1) *A n.a.s.c. in order that the quadratic form in (y, φ)*

$$-\dot{V} = y'Cy + \rho\varphi^2 + 2\varphi\, d'y$$

be positive definite is that $C > 0$ and (F_i) hold.

Now in Reference [2] Yacubovich obtained the following result:

(3.2) *A n.a.s.c. for the positive definiteness of the same form is that there exists a real vector $g = d/\sqrt{\rho}$ such that $C - gg' > 0$.*

Evidently the two statements are equivalent. To show that this is indeed the case one merely needs to "complete the squares" in two different manners. Incidentally there will result a new derivation of the inequality (F_i).

The "square completing" corresponding to (3.1) is indicated by:

$$-\dot{V} = (y' + \varphi d'C^{-1})C(y + \varphi C^{-1}d) + (\rho - d'C^{-1}d)\varphi^2$$

and it is plain that, since $C > 0$, $-\dot{V}$ is positive definite if, and only if, (F_i) holds.

The square completing corresponding to (3.2) is

$$-\dot{V} = y'Cy + \rho\left(\varphi + y'\frac{d}{\sqrt{\rho}}\right)\left(\varphi + \frac{d'}{\sqrt{\rho}}y\right) - y'\frac{dd'}{\rho}y$$

$$= y'\left(C - \frac{dd'}{\rho}\right)y + \rho\left(\varphi + y'\frac{d}{\sqrt{\rho}}\right)\left(\varphi + \frac{d'}{\sqrt{\rho}}y\right).$$

REMARKS. I. The only conditions imposed upon the control parameters are (2.5) and (F_i).

II. Actually a less stringent road to absolute stability is often available. Namely, according to a result of LaSalle (see IX, 4.8) it is often sufficient to have $-\dot{V} \geqq 0$ provided that $y = 0$, $\sigma = 0$ is the only solution of (2.3) in $\dot{V} = 0$. However to prove this fact frequently requires considerable labor. It has therefore seemed best to adhere to the general rule.

§4. On the Utilization of Certain Complex Coordinate Systems

Referring to (IX, §1) one may have occasion to utilize a complex coordinate system in which a real point x is represented as follows:

$$x_1,..., x_p, \quad \bar{x}_1,..., \bar{x}_p, \quad x_{2p+1},..., x_n$$

where the last $q = n - 2p$ coordinates are real. In particular the real vectors b, c have components

$$b_1,..., b_p, \quad \bar{b}_1,..., \bar{b}_p, \quad b_{2p+1},..., b_n$$

$$c_1,..., c_p, \quad \bar{c}_1,..., \bar{c}_p, \quad c_{2p+1},..., c_n$$

with the last q components real. The associated matrix A is in the Jordan normal form as described in (IX, §1). This time, if the matrices B, C are hermitian (positive definite), there takes place the *Liapunov complex relation*.

$$A^*B + BA = -C,$$

and B is still unique. Upon introducing for convenience $\varphi = \bar{\varphi}$, one takes naturally

$$V(y, \sigma) = y^*By + \Phi(\sigma).$$

Since now

$$\dot{\sigma} = c^*y - \rho\varphi(\sigma),$$

one finds

$$-\dot{V} = y^*Cy + \rho\varphi\bar{\varphi} + (\bar{\varphi}d^*y + \varphi y^*d),$$

23

where as before

$$d = Bb - \tfrac{1}{2}c.$$

Since Sylvester's theorem holds for hermitian forms, or else utilizing the reduction of §3 leading to (3.1), we have this time instead of (F_i)

(F_i^*) $\qquad\qquad\qquad\qquad \rho > d^*C^{-1}d$

with $C > 0$ as n.a.s.c. to have $-\dot{V}$ positive definite hermitian in (y, φ).

Since *real* quadratic forms are merely *special* hermitian forms, the present development includes the earlier theory.

§5. Special Cases

Since after all C is a completely arbitrary matrix >0 one may specialize it and obtain a simpler form of (F_i) or (F_i^*). Take in particular $C = E$. Then (F_i) or (F_i^*) reduces to

(5.1) $\qquad\qquad\qquad \rho > d^*d = \|d\|^2.$

This may be achieved by using a special coordinate system in which $C = E$.

Of more interest is the case where the matrix A is relatively simple. Suppose that $A \sim \operatorname{diag}(\lambda_1,..., \lambda_n)$, so that the λ_h are the characteristic roots of A. Assume the coordinates so chosen that actually $A = \operatorname{diag}(\lambda_1,..., \lambda_n)$. This will be called the *standard example*. Set once and for all

(5.2) $\qquad\qquad\qquad \operatorname{Re} \lambda_h = -\mu_h > 0.$

Referring to (IX, 3.9) we have this time

$$b_{jk} = \frac{-c_{jk}}{\bar{\lambda}_j + \lambda_k}.$$

Hence the components of $d = Bb - \tfrac{1}{2}c$ are

$$d_j = -\tfrac{1}{2}c_j - \sum_k \frac{c_{jk}b_k}{\bar{\lambda}_j + \lambda_k}$$

and we obtain directly $d^*C^{-1}d$ in terms of C.

Take in particular $C = \operatorname{diag}(\alpha_1,..., \alpha_n)$, $\alpha_h > 0$. As a consequence

$$B = \operatorname{diag}\left(\frac{\alpha_1}{2\mu_1},..., \frac{\alpha_n}{2\mu_n}\right),$$

$$Bb - \tfrac{1}{2}c = \left(\frac{\alpha_1 b_1}{2\mu_1} - \tfrac{1}{2}c_1, ..., \frac{\alpha_n b_n}{2\mu_n} - \tfrac{1}{2}c_n \right).$$

Thus (F_i) assumes the form

$$\rho > \frac{1}{4} \sum \frac{1}{\alpha_h} \left(\frac{\alpha_h b_h}{\mu_h} - c_h \right) \left(\frac{\alpha_h \bar{b}_h}{\mu_h} - \bar{c}_h \right).$$

Let $\alpha_h = \beta_h{}^2$, $\beta_h > 0$. Then

(5.3)
$$\rho > \frac{1}{4} \sum \left(\frac{\beta_h b_h}{\mu_h} - \frac{c_h}{\beta_h} \right) \left(\frac{\beta_h \bar{b}_h}{\mu_h} - \frac{\bar{c}_h}{\beta_h} \right).$$

The sum is a function of the variables β_h, which are as yet purely arbitrary, except that they must be real and positive. If we obtain a minimum of this sum we will have a lower bound for ρ. To minimize the sum one merely has to minimize its individual terms, i.e. terms of the form

$$F(\beta) = \left(\frac{\beta b}{\mu} - \frac{c}{\beta} \right) \left(\frac{\beta \bar{b}}{\mu} - \frac{\bar{c}}{\beta} \right).$$

Here one must distinguish several cases.

A. λ *is real, hence b and c are also real.* Then

$$F(\beta) = \left(\frac{\beta b}{\mu} - \frac{c}{\beta} \right)^2.$$

If $c = 0$ the minimum of $F(\beta)$ is obtained for $\beta = 0$ and then $F(0) = 0$. If $b = 0, c \neq 0$, the lowest bound of $F(\beta)$ corresponds to $\beta = \infty$ and is again zero. It is obviously zero if $b = c = 0$.

Suppose $bc \neq 0$ and say $bc < 0$. One may assume that $b < 0, c > 0$. Now

$$F'(\beta) = 2 \left(\frac{b}{\mu} + \frac{c}{\beta^2} \right) \left(\frac{\beta b}{\mu} - \frac{c}{\beta} \right).$$

The second factor is $\neq 0$, so that $F'(\beta) = 0$ only for $\beta^2 = -c\mu/b$. Hence, $F_{\min}(\beta) = |4bc/\mu|$.

Suppose now $bc > 0$. We may take $b > 0, c > 0$. Then in $F'(\beta)$ the second factor alone may vanish and the minimum is zero. Note that in both cases

$$\alpha = \mu \left| \frac{c}{b} \right|.$$

B. λ_h *is complex, hence* b_h *and* c_h *are both complex.*
This time one must deal directly with $F(\beta)$. Here

$$F(\beta) = \beta^2 \frac{b\bar{b}}{\mu^2} - \frac{b\bar{c} + \bar{b}c}{\mu} + \frac{c\bar{c}}{\beta^2}.$$

The cases $b = 0$ or $c = 0$ yield the same result as before. We may therefore assume that $bc \neq 0$. Now

$$F'(\beta) = \frac{2\beta b\bar{b}}{\mu^2} - \frac{2c\bar{c}}{\beta^3} = 0$$

for $\beta^2 = \alpha = \mu\sqrt{c\bar{c}/b\bar{b}} = \mu|c/b|$ (as before) and the minimum is

$$F_{\min} = \frac{(\sqrt{b\bar{c}} - \sqrt{\bar{b}c})^2}{\mu} = \frac{4(\mathrm{Im}\sqrt{\bar{b}c})^2}{\mu}.$$

For the real case, this expression coincides with the one already obtained. Therefore, finally one obtains for ρ the lower bound

(5.4)
$$\rho > \sum \frac{(\mathrm{Im}\sqrt{\bar{b}_h c_h})^2}{\mu_h}.$$

Chapter 3

INDIRECT CONTROLS (continued)

The general theory developed in the preceding chapter presents a number of side questions to be discussed in the present chapter.

§1. Invariance under Change of Coordinates

There have been obtained two inequalities involving expressions depending upon the coordinates, namely (II, 2.5) and (F_i). We shall show that *these inequalities do not depend upon the coordinate system.* To be precise, let $y = Py_0$ be a transformation of coordinates and let $A_0, B_0,...,$ be the expressions corresponding to $A, B,...,$ in the new coordinates. Let also (F_i^0), $(II, 2.5)^0$ correspond to (F_i) and (II, 2.5) in the new coordinates. We propose to prove:

(1.1) (F_i) *and* (II, 2.5) *are respectively equivalent to* (F_i^0) *and* $(II, 2.5)^0$.

This means that one is free to express these inequalities in any convenient coordinate system.

The transformation $y = Py_0$ gives rise to a new system

$$\dot{y}_0 = P^{-1}APy_0 - \varphi(\sigma)P^{-1}b$$

$$\dot{\sigma} = c'Py_0 - \rho\varphi(\sigma).$$

27

Hence

$$A_0 = P^{-1}AP, \qquad b_0 = P^{-1}b, \qquad c_0' = c'P.$$

Consequently

$$y'Py = y_0'P'BPy_0$$

so that $B_0 = P'BP$, and also at once $c_0'A_0^{-1}b_0 = c'A^{-1}b$. This proves the invariance of the inequality (II, 2.5).

We also have

$$d_0 = B_0 b_0 - \tfrac{1}{2}c_0 = P'BPP^{-1}b - \tfrac{1}{2}P'c = P'd.$$

Moreover

$$C_0^{-1} = (P'CP)^{-1} = P^{-1}C^{-1}P'^{-1},$$

and therefore

$$d_0'C_0^{-1}d_0 = d'PP^{-1}C^{-1}P'^{-1}P'd = d'C^{-1}d.$$

Since ρ is invariant we have

$$\rho - d'C^{-1}d = \rho_0 - d_0'C_0^{-1}d_0$$

so that (F_i) is likewise invariant.

§2. Reduction of the Number of Conditions on the Control Parameters

A variety of conditions have been imposed upon the control parameters b, c, ρ, $\varphi(\sigma)$. As we shall see, these conditions are far from independent and hence can be sharply reduced in number. They are:

On $\varphi(\sigma)$: properties I, II, III of (I, §1); notably III has been imposed to guarantee asymptotic stability in the large, i.e. in particular, that every solution $(y(t), \sigma(t))$ of (II, 2.3) $\to 0$ as $t \to +\infty$.

On b, c, ρ:

(2.1) $$\rho \neq c'A^{-1}b,$$

likewise (F_i) for some $C > 0$. Actually it was shown in (II, 2.12) that, indirectly $C > 0$ plus (F_i) imply (2.1). A more complete result is the following proposition due to LaSalle [1].

(2.2) **Theorem of LaSalle.** *Let A be stable and C (hence B) > 0. Then*

(2.3) $$d'C^{-1}d > c'A^{-1}b.$$

28

Moreover theorem (II, 2.11) *is still valid without imposing on* $\varphi(\sigma)$ *property* III *of* I, §1 (*divergence of the integral* $\Phi(\sigma)$ *as* $\sigma \to \pm\infty$).

(2.3a) *Corollary.* $C > 0$ *plus* (F_i) *imply* (2.1) *in the stronger form* $\rho > c'A^{-1}b$.

REMARK. A weaker form of (2.3) was obtained earlier by Yacubovich.

PROOF OF (2.3). This is the crux of the matter and the more difficult part of the argument: we first show that if x, y are two n vectors then

$$(2.4) \qquad (Bx - y)'C^{-1}(Bx - y) \geqq 2y'A^{-1}x.$$

By choosing $x = b$ and $y = \frac{1}{2}c$, this yields

$$(2.5) \qquad d'C^{-1}d \geqq -c'A^{-1}b,$$

which is (2.3). Thus, we have to prove (2.4). This will be done through another relation.

Incidentally the necessity of the relation

$$(2.6) \qquad \rho \neq c'A^{-1}b$$

for absolute stability was also proved in (II, §2).

Let, then, u, v be two arbitrary n vectors, and Q an $n \times n$ matrix such that

$$(2.7) \qquad Q + Q' > 0.$$

Note that in view of $u'(Qu) = (Qu)'u = u'Q'u$, we have

$$(2.8) \qquad u'Qu = \tfrac{1}{2}u'(Q + Q')u > 0 \qquad \text{for all} \quad u \neq 0.$$

Moreover (2.8) implies that Q is nonsingular. For otherwise there would exist a vector $u \neq 0$ such that $Qu = 0$ and hence $u'Qu = 0$. It follows that Q^{-1} exists. Now in replacing in (2.8) u by $Q^{-1}u \neq 0$ if $u \neq 0$, there follows $u'(Q^{-1})'Q \cdot (Q^{-1}u) = u'(Q^{-1})'u$ if $u \neq 0$. Hence also

$$(2.9) \qquad u' \cdot Q^{-1}u > 0$$

if $u \neq 0$. Thus actually Q^{-1} likewise satisfies the relation (2.7) (Q replaced by Q^{-1}).

Let now

$$\alpha = (u' + v')(Q + Q')(u + v) - 2u'(Q + Q')Q^{-1}(Q + Q')v,$$

$$\beta = 2(u'Q' - v'Q)Q^{-1}(Qu - Q'v).$$

29

From (2.9) one infers that $\beta \geqq 0$. On the other hand by expanding both α and β one verifies that $\alpha = \beta$ and so $\alpha \geqq 0$.

Upon replacing now u and v in α by $(Q + Q')^{-1}u$ and $(Q + Q')^{-1}v$ there follows

$$(u' + v')(Q + Q')^{-1}(u + v) - 2u'Q^{-1}v \geqq 0.$$

Set now $Q = -BA, u = -y, v = Bx$. This is legitimate since

$$Q + Q' = -(A'B + BA) = C > 0.$$

There results then

$$-(Bx - y)'(A'B + BA)^{-1}(Bx - y) \geqq 2y'A^{-1}x$$

which is precisely (2.4). Thus (2.4) is proved and so is (2.3).

Since $\rho - c'A^{-1}b > 0$, the transformation $(x, \xi) \to (y, \sigma)$ of (II, 2.2), is justified and so we are at liberty to keep on operating with the variables y, σ, that is with the system (II, 2.3).

PROOF THAT $\|y(t)\| + |\sigma(t)| \to 0$ *as* $t \to +\infty$. Under our assumptions the function

$$V(y, \sigma) = y'By + \Phi(\sigma)$$

is positive definite and $\dot{V}$ is negative definite throughout the space (y, σ). Hence (Liapunov, IX, 4.5) the origin is asymptotically stable. Referring to LaSalle and Lefschetz [1, p. 66, Theorem VIII], it is therefore sufficient to show that the solution $(y(t), \sigma(t))$ is bounded. The first step is to show that it is defined in the future, that is, that there is no finite positive T such that $\|y(t)\| + |\sigma(t)| \to \infty$ as $t \to T$ from below. Take any $0 < t_0 < T$. Since $\dot{V} < 0$ we have for $t > t_0$:

$$V_0 = V(y(t_0), \sigma(t_0)) > V(y(t), \sigma(t)).$$

There is also an $\alpha > 0$ such that

$$y'By \geqq \alpha\|y\|^2$$

for all y. Hence for $t > t_0$

$$V_0 > \alpha\|y(t)\|^2 + \Phi(\sigma(t)).$$

Therefore $\|y(t)\|$ is bounded for $t = T$ and so for all t. Moreover $\Phi(\sigma(t))$ is also bounded. This may happen through $\sigma(t)$ being bounded for all t, or else through $|\sigma(t)| \to \infty$ with t. All that is required is to exclude this second possibility.

Suppose then that $|\sigma(t)| \to \infty$. As a consequence for some T and $t \geq T$, $\sigma(t)$ will have a fixed sign, say $\sigma(t) > 0$. (The case $\sigma(t) < 0$ would be treated in the same way.) Now

$$\dot{\sigma} - c'y = \dot{\sigma} - c'(A^{-1}\dot{y} + A^{-1}b\varphi(\sigma)) = -\rho\varphi(\sigma).$$

Hence in view of (2.3a)

$$\frac{d}{dt}(\sigma(t) - c'A^{-1}y(t)) = -(\rho - c'A^{-1}b)\varphi(\sigma) < 0.$$

Since by hypothesis $\sigma(t) \to +\infty$ with t, and since $\|y(t)\|$ remains finite we may choose T so large that for $t \geq T$ we have

$$\sigma(t) - c'A^{-1}y(t) > 0.$$

Upon integrating then from T to t we obtain

$$[\sigma(t) - c'A^{-1}y(t)]_T^t < 0.$$

As a consequence, since $\|y(t)\|$ is bounded, so is $\sigma(t)$. This completes the proof of the theorem.

§3. Lurie's Method and a Variant

By taking a more restricted type of matrix C and assuming that the characteristic roots of the matrix A are all distinct, Lurie obtained a narrower sufficiency condition for absolute stability than the inequality (F_i). In presenting these results we will operate at once with complex coordinates, that is take the situation of (II, §4). Now Lurie's choice of B and C is as follows:

$$C = a\bar{a}' + \mathrm{diag}(\alpha_1, ..., \alpha_n), \qquad \alpha_h > 0$$

$$B = -\left(\frac{\bar{a}_j a_k}{\lambda_j + \lambda_k}\right) + \mathrm{diag}\left(\frac{\alpha_1}{2\mu_1}, ..., \frac{\alpha_n}{2\mu_n}\right)$$

where

$$\lambda_j = -\mu_j + iv_j, \qquad \mu_j > 0.$$

Note that

$$y * Cy = y * a^* y + \sum \mu_h y_h \bar{y}_h$$

$$= \left(\sum a_h y_h\right)\left(\sum \bar{a}_h \bar{y}_h\right) + \sum \alpha_h y_h \bar{y}_h > 0 \qquad \text{for} \quad y \neq 0.$$

31

Hence likewise $B > 0$ (mere verification).

Then Lurie completes the squares in the expression of $-\dot{V}$ and obtains cross products of type y^*y, whose coefficients, set equal to zero, give *sufficient conditions* for absolute stability. The computations are definitely involved and we merely reproduce the final result with mild changes of notation. Observing that the only condition on the α_h are that they be positive, we find for the Lurie system under the general Lurie assumption that every $b_j = -1$:

$$(3.1) \qquad \bar{a}_j \sum \frac{a_k}{\lambda_j + \lambda_k} - \tfrac{1}{2}c_j - \bar{a}_j\sqrt{\rho} \geqq 0 \qquad (j = 1, 2,..., n).$$

His conclusion is that if one can find a real point a such that all the inequalities (3.1) *are satisfied then the control is absolutely stable.*

A variant. Observe that a simpler way to guarantee that $-\dot{V}$ be positive definite is to take

$$(3.2) \qquad d = Bb - \tfrac{1}{2}c = 0.$$

With B, C and the general situation unchanged, the system (3.2) yields

$$(3.3) \qquad -\bar{a}_j \sum \frac{a_k b_k}{\lambda_j + \lambda_k} + \frac{\alpha_j b_j}{2\mu_j} - \tfrac{1}{2}c_j = 0, \qquad j = 1, 2,..., n.$$

If one assumes, as done throughout in Lurie's equation that every $b_j = -1$ then (3.3) reduces to (3.2), except of course, for the additional term in $\sqrt{\rho}$. Our system is thus mildly more complicated, but the difference is not really significant. However, its derivation is altogether simpler than that of Lurie.

REMARKS. I. As observed by the author in a recent paper (Lefschetz [3]) the relation (3.2) was utilized earlier and independently by Mufti.

II. The number of parameters in the matrix C of Lurie's special type is $2n$. Since it is not certain that they are independent, one may say that his system depends on at most $2n$ parameters. On the other hand, the general system: C arbitrary positive, depends upon $n(n + 1)/2$ parameters and this number $> 2n$ for $n \geqq 4$.

In point of fact for $n = 2$ the two systems depend upon three parameters—not the apparent four since three is the maximum possible.

Thus, for $n \geqq 4$, the class of Lurie matrices C is definitely special.

§4. Application to Systems of Order Two

We shall take advantage of the low dimension to study our system (§3, variant) more fully. And specifically, we shall discuss at length the properties of the relation (3.2).

First, a preliminary remark. We will assume the coordinates y_1, y_2 so chosen that the matrix A is in one of the Jordan normal forms. Moreover, we will also suppose that under these coordinates the vector b has both components $b_1, b_2 \neq 0$. Observe that from the control point of view, if e.g. $b_1 = 0$, the first equation of the system reads

$$\dot{y}_1 = \lambda_1 y_1$$

which indicates that y_1 is *not affected* by the operation of the control. In other words, practically speaking the control is only *partly* effective. Thus, our assumption that both $b_1, b_2 \neq 0$ means that the control is completely effective.

Under our assumption then, the change of coordinates $y_j \rightarrow b_j y_j$, $j = 1, 2$ will yield the same system but with

$$-b = \begin{pmatrix} 1 \\ 1 \end{pmatrix}.$$

This scheme will somewhat simplify the calculations. We continue to assume, of course, that the matrix A is stable. There are then the following three possible normal forms for A:

I. $\operatorname{diag}(\lambda_1, \lambda_2)$, λ_1 and λ_2 real and < 0.

II. $\begin{pmatrix} \lambda & 0 \\ 1 & \lambda \end{pmatrix}$, λ real and < 0.

III. $\operatorname{diag}(\lambda, \bar{\lambda})$, λ complex.

The following notations will be used:

I. $\lambda_1 = -\mu_1 < 0$, $\lambda_2 = -\mu_2 < 0$;

II. $\lambda = -\mu < 0$;

III. $\lambda = -\mu + iv$, $\mu > 0$.

33

Thus, the three normal forms are:

I. $$\operatorname{diag}(-\mu_1, -\mu_2);$$

II. $$\begin{pmatrix} -\mu & 0 \\ 1 & -\mu \end{pmatrix};$$

III. $$\operatorname{diag}(-\mu + iv, -\mu - iv).$$

CASE I. The system to be discussed is then

$$\dot{y}_1 = -\mu_1 y_1 + \varphi(\sigma)$$

(4.1) $$\dot{y}_2 = -\mu_2 y_2 + \varphi(\sigma)$$

$$\dot{\sigma} = c_1 y_1 + c_2 y_2 - \rho\varphi(\sigma).$$

Choose now

$$C = \begin{pmatrix} p & q \\ q & r \end{pmatrix}.$$

As we assume $C > 0$ we must have

(4.2) $$p > 0, \qquad pr - q^2 > 0.$$

As a consequence, it is known that

$$B = \begin{pmatrix} p_0 & q_0 \\ q_0 & r_0 \end{pmatrix} > 0,$$

(4.3) $$p_0 = \frac{p}{2\mu_1}, \qquad q_0 = \frac{q}{\mu_1 + \mu_2}, \qquad r_0 = \frac{r}{2\mu_2}.$$

Then (3.2) yields

$$p_0 + q_0 + \tfrac{1}{2}c_1 = 0$$

(4.4) $$q_0 + r_0 + \tfrac{1}{2}c_2 = 0.$$

The inequalities (4.2) are seen at once to be equivalent to the following:

$$p_0 > 0, \qquad p_0 r_0 - \varepsilon q_0^{\,2} > 0$$

(4.5) $$\varepsilon = \frac{(\mu_1 + \mu_2)^2}{4\mu_1\mu_2} \geq 1.$$

34

Upon expressing p_0 and r_0 in terms of q_0 from the relations (4.4) and substituting in (4.5) there follows;

$$(4.6) \qquad g(q_0) = (\varepsilon - 1)q_0{}^2 - \tfrac{1}{2}(c_1 + c_2)q_0 - \tfrac{1}{4}c_1 c_2 < 0.$$

Suppose first $\varepsilon > 1$. The discriminant of $g(q_0)$ is

$$\delta = \frac{(c_1 - c_2)^2 + 4\varepsilon c_1 c_2}{4}.$$

If $\delta \leq 0$ and since $\varepsilon > 1$ the inequality (4.6) does not hold. That is the present scheme based on (3.2) does not lead to a sufficiency condition for absolute stability. Assume $\delta > 0$. Then $g(q_0)$ has two distinct real roots q_1, q_2. One can only satisfy (4.6) by taking q_0 in the interval (q_1, q_2). On the other hand, $p_0 > 0$ requires $q_0 < -\tfrac{1}{2}c_1$. Now

$$g(-\tfrac{1}{2}c_1) = \varepsilon c_1{}^2/4 > 0.$$

Hence $-\tfrac{1}{2}c_1$ is not in the interval (q_1, q_2). Hence $q_0 < -\tfrac{1}{2}c_1$ can only be fulfilled if $\tfrac{1}{2}(q_1 + q_2) < -\tfrac{1}{2}c_1$, or

$$-\tfrac{1}{2}c_1 > \frac{c_1 + c_2}{4(\varepsilon - 1)}$$

or finally

$$(4.7) \qquad\qquad (2\varepsilon - 1)c_1 < -c_2$$

$$(4.7a) \qquad\qquad (c_1 - c_2)^2 + 4\varepsilon c_1 c_2 > 0.$$

Thus, if $\varepsilon \neq 1$, i.e. $\mu_1 \neq \mu_2$ or equivalently $\lambda_1 \neq \lambda_2$ both being real, the inequalities (4.7), (4.7a) together with $\rho > 0$ express sufficient conditions for absolute stability. We will then have an appropriate value of q_0, hence from (4.4) appropriate values of r_0, and so appropriate p, q, r from (4.3).

Suppose now that $\varepsilon = 1$, i.e., that $\lambda_1 = \lambda_2 = -\mu < 0$. We still have, of course, $A = \operatorname{diag}(\lambda, \lambda)$. Here (4.6) reduces to

$$2(c_1 + c_2)q_0 + c_1 c_2 > 0.$$

If $c_1 + c_2 \neq 0$, this yields

$$(4.8) \qquad\qquad q_0 \gtrless \frac{1}{2}\frac{-c_1 c_2}{c_1 + c_2} \qquad \text{if} \quad c_1 + c_2 \gtrless 0,$$

a condition that may always be satisfied. Hence, again we will have appropriate values of q_0, p_0, r_0 and so likewise of p, q, r.

Finally, if $c_1 + c_2 = 0$ (4.7a) demands that $(c_1 + c_2) < 0$, which does not hold. Thus, also in the present instance, one cannot verify absolute stability on the strength of the system (3.2).

CASE II. Normal form

$$\begin{pmatrix} -\mu & 0 \\ 1 & -\mu \end{pmatrix}.$$

Since μ is real, we take again

(4.9)
$$C = \begin{pmatrix} p & q \\ q & r \end{pmatrix}$$

and we have the inequalities (4.2). One must solve for B from Liapunov's relation

(4.10)
$$A'B + BA = -C.$$

Set once more

$$B = \begin{pmatrix} p_0 & q_0 \\ q_0 & r_0 \end{pmatrix}.$$

Then from (4.10)

$$\begin{pmatrix} p_0 & q_0 \\ q_0 & r_0 \end{pmatrix}\begin{pmatrix} \lambda & 0 \\ 1 & \lambda \end{pmatrix} + \begin{pmatrix} \lambda & 1 \\ 0 & \lambda \end{pmatrix}\begin{pmatrix} p_0 & q_0 \\ q_0 & r_0 \end{pmatrix} = -\begin{pmatrix} p & q \\ q & r \end{pmatrix}.$$

Upon identifying corresponding terms and noting that $\lambda = -\mu < 0$, one finds the relations

$$2(p_0\mu - q_0) = p, \qquad (2q_0\mu - r_0) = q, \qquad 2r_0\mu = r.$$

Observing that in view of the second inequality (4.2) the first may be replaced by $r > 0$, we find from (4.2) the necessary inequalities

$$4r_0\mu(p_0\mu - q_0) - (2q_0\mu - r_0)^2 > 0, \qquad r_0 > 0.$$

Upon substituting for p_0 and r_0 from (4.4) there follows

$$4\mu(\tfrac{1}{2}c_2 + q_0)((\tfrac{1}{2}c_1 + q_0)\mu + q_0) - (2q_0\mu + (\tfrac{1}{2}c_2 + q_0))^2 > 0$$

$$\tfrac{1}{2}c_2 + q_0 < 0.$$

Upon setting $\frac{1}{2}c_2 + q_0 = S$, this system reduces ultimately to

$$S^2 - 2\mu^2(c_1 + c_2)S + \mu^2 c_2 < 0$$

(4.11)

$$S < 0.$$

Let $f(S)$ denote the above quadratic in S. Since $f(S) < 0$ for some S, the two roots S_1, S_2 of $f(S) = 0$ must be real and there must be negative numbers in the interval (S_1, S_2). Since $S_1 S_2 = \mu^2 c_2{}^2 > 0$ the two roots have the same sign and so both must be negative. Hence, we must have $S_1 + S_2 < 0$. Thus, our conditions are

(a) $\quad \mu^2(c_1 + c_2)^2 > c_2{}^2$

(4.12)

(b) $\quad c_1 + c_2 < 0.$

To sum up in the present case if (4.12) holds and S is chosen between S_1 and S_2 absolute stability is guaranteed.

CASE III. *Characteristic roots $\lambda, \bar{\lambda}$.* The system is now

$$\dot{y} = \lambda y + \varphi(\sigma)$$

(4.13)

$$\dot{\bar{y}} = \bar{\lambda}\bar{y} + \varphi(\sigma)$$

$$\dot{\sigma} = cy + \bar{c}\bar{y} - \rho\varphi(\sigma).$$

This time C must be a positive definite hermitian matrix e.g.

$$C = \begin{pmatrix} p & q \\ \bar{q} & p \end{pmatrix}, \quad p \text{ real.}$$

The condition $C > 0$ requires that

(4.14) $$p > 0, \quad p^2 - q\bar{q} > 0.$$

Then if

$$B = \frac{1}{2}\begin{pmatrix} p_0 & q_0 \\ \bar{q}_0 & p_0 \end{pmatrix},$$

we have

$$p_0 = \frac{p}{\mu} \quad , \quad q_0 = \frac{q}{\mu + iv} \quad , \quad r_0 = \frac{r}{\mu} \quad .$$

37

This time (3.2) yields

(4.15)
$$p_0 + q_0 + c = 0.$$

From (4.15) follows

(4.16)
$$p = \mu p_0 = -\mu(c + q_0).$$

Hence from (4.14)

$$\mu^2(c + q_0)(\bar{c} + \bar{q}_0) - (\mu^2 + v^2)q_0\bar{q}_0 > 0.$$

Upon setting $\varepsilon = v^2/\mu^2$ this inequality reduces to

(4.17)
$$g(q_0) = c\bar{c} + q_0\bar{c} + \bar{q}_0c - \varepsilon q_0\bar{q}_0 > 0.$$

We also have from (4.14) and (4.16) that $c + q_0$ must be real and negative. Hence we may write

$$c = \alpha + i\beta, \qquad q_0 = \gamma - i\beta,$$

where

(4.18)
$$\alpha + \gamma < 0.$$

From (4.17) there follows as a condition

$$h(\alpha) = \alpha^2 + 2\gamma\alpha - (1 + \varepsilon)\beta^2 - \varepsilon\gamma^2 > 0.$$

Since we dispose of q let us choose it so that $\gamma \neq 0$. Denote by α_1, α_2 the two roots of $h(\alpha)$. Since $\alpha_1\alpha_2 < 0$ both are real and of opposite sign, and α must be between them. Let $\alpha_1 < 0$. Since $h(-\gamma) < 0$, $-\gamma$ is between the roots. Hence in order that (4.18) hold, one must take $\alpha < \alpha_1$. If that is done the present scheme based on (3.2) will effectively guarantee absolute stability.

Chapter 4

DIRECT CONTROLS, LINEARIZATION, AND MULTIPLE FEEDBACK

§1. Direct Control: General Case

The basic system is

(1.1)
$$\dot{x} = Ax - \varphi(\sigma)b$$
$$\sigma = c'x$$

where A continues to be a stable matrix and $\varphi(\sigma)$ is the usual characteristic function. The system is of the same order n as the state system $\dot{x} = Ax$. We refer again to the Introduction for existence and uniqueness of solutions. The problem continues to be to find sufficient conditions for absolute stability.

At all events for absolute stability the origin must be the only critical point. That is, the only solution of

(1.2)
$$Ax - \varphi(\sigma)b = Ax - \varphi(c'x)b = 0$$

must be $x = 0$. In the absence of more information about $\varphi(\sigma)$, all that one can do is to assume explicitly that this condition is fulfilled.

In a moment $\dot{\sigma}$ will be required. Here

(1.3)
$$\dot{\sigma} = c'\dot{x} = c'Ax - \varphi(\sigma)c'b.$$

Upon setting

(1.4) $$c_0 = A'c, \qquad \rho_0 = c'b$$

the relation (1.3) assumes the more familiar form

$$\dot{\sigma} = c_0'x - \rho_0\varphi(\sigma).$$

In the search for absolute stability the temptation is great to follow the same path as for indirect controls. Unfortunately this turns out to be only partly possible.

Take the same Liapunov function as in (II, §2):

(1.5) $$V(x) = x'Bx + \Phi(\sigma).$$

Here again

(1.6) $$-\dot{V} = x'Cx + 2d'x\varphi + c'b\varphi^2$$

$$A'B + BA = -C$$

$$d = Bb - \tfrac{1}{2}A'c.$$

Choose once more $C > 0$, and as a consequence $B > 0$. Hence $V(x)$ is positive definite for all x and $\to\infty$ with $\|x\|$. Thus V still behaves satisfactorily. Not so, however, regarding $\dot{V}$. We still have (as in II, §3):

(1.7) $$-\dot{V} = (x + C^{-1} d\varphi)'C(x + C^{-1} d\varphi) + (c'b - d'C^{-1} d)\varphi^2,$$

and one would like to adopt

(1.7a) $$c'b > d'C^{-1} d$$

as a condition. However

(1.8) $$\dot{V} = (2Bx - c\varphi)'\dot{x} = (2Bx - c\varphi)'(Ax - b\varphi).$$

This shows that $\dot{V}$ cannot be *formally* a definite quadratic form in the independent variables x and φ since, for example, one may have $Ax - b\varphi = 0$ for x, φ not both zero. The best that one may achieve is $\dot{V} \leq 0$, and this will follow if we impose

(1.9) $$c'b = d'C^{-1} d.$$

since then by (1.7)

(1.10) $$-\dot{V} = (x + C^{-1} d\varphi)'C(x + C^{-1} d\varphi)$$

40

It is clear from the above that in the $(n + 1)$-dimensional space x, φ (φ considered as independent of x) $-\dot{V}$ is positive semidefinite and furthermore (since $C > 0$) $-\dot{V}$ is zero only on a one-dimensional subspace of the space of x and φ. Now we shall make $-\dot{V}$ positive definite in x alone. By looking at (1.8) we can see that $-\dot{V}$ is zero when $Ax - b\varphi$ is zero and since A is stable this system of equations has a one-dimensional subspace of solutions. Thus $-\dot{V}$ is zero if and only if $Ax - b\varphi = 0$. Now we take into account that x and φ do not in fact vary independently. We have already assumed that the only critical point for (1.1) is the origin, hence $Ax - b\varphi(c'x)$ is not zero and $-\dot{V}$ is positive definite in x alone. Thus the system (1.1) is absolutely stable.

An easy way to find that the origin is the only critical point is this: let $A - \mu bc'$ be nonsingular for all $\mu > 0$, but that for some x_0: $Ax_0 - b\varphi(c'x_0) = 0$. Now $\varphi(c'x_0) = \mu_0 c'x_0$, for some $\mu_0 > 0$. Hence $(A - \mu_0 bc')x_0 = 0$ which implies $x_0 = 0$. We shall show later (§4) that $|A - \mu bc'| = |A|(1 - \mu c'A^{-1}b) \neq 0$. Hence $|A - \mu bc'| \neq 0$ for all $\mu > 0$ if and only if $c'A^{-1}b \leqq 0$.

(1.1) **Theorem.** *If* (1.9) *holds,* $C > 0$, *and* $c'A^{-1}b \leqq 0$ *the system* (1.1) *is absolutely stable.*

A more flexible situation is discussed in §§6, 7. In my paper [3] I wrongly used (1.7a). This was recently indicated in Aizerman and Gantmacher [1, p. 18].

§2. Direct Control, Standard Example

An interesting special case is the standard example of (II, §5). In this case A is taken as $\mathrm{diag}(\lambda_1, \lambda_2, ..., \lambda_n)$ where the $\lambda_h = -\mu_h$ are real and negative.

As in (II, §5) take $C = \mathrm{diag}(\alpha_1, ..., \alpha_n)$, $\alpha_h > 0$ and as a consequence

$$B = \mathrm{diag}\left(\frac{\alpha_1}{2\mu_1}, ..., \frac{\alpha_n}{2\mu_n}\right)$$

and

$$d = Bb - \tfrac{1}{2}A'c = \left(\frac{\alpha_1 b_1}{2\mu_1} + \tfrac{1}{2}\mu_1 c_1, ..., \frac{\alpha_n b_n}{2\mu_n} + \tfrac{1}{2}\mu_n c_n\right)$$

41

Thus (1.9) assumes the form

$$\sum c_n b_n = \sum \frac{1}{4\alpha_h} \left\{ \frac{\alpha_h b_h}{\mu_h} + \mu_h c_h \right\}^2$$

or

$$\sum \frac{1}{4\alpha_h} \left\{ \frac{\alpha_h b_h}{\mu_h} - \mu_h c_h \right\}^2 = 0.$$

The above equality can be satisfied if and only if $\alpha_h = \mu_h^2(c_h/b_h)$ if we make the physically reasonable assumption that the b_h and c_h are not zero. The inequality $\alpha_h > 0$ implies $c_h b_h > 0$. Since $c'A^{-1}b = -\Sigma(c_h b_h/\mu_h)$ the condition that every $c_h b_h > 0$ implies $c'A^{-1}b < 0$ and hence the origin is the only critical point (II, 2.5 and 1.4).

Thus *a sufficient condition for absolute stability of* (1.9) *when* $A = \operatorname{diag}(\lambda_1,...,\lambda_n)$, $\lambda_h < 0$, *is that every* $c_h b_h > 0$.

One should not be deceived by the greater mathematical simplicity of the equations for direct control. If one tries to use the Lurie variant for case I of (III, §4) one finds that the conditions cannot be satisfied. In this case (1.9) becomes

$$c_1 + c_2 = 0$$

and the inequality (4.6) of III becomes

$$(\varepsilon - 1)q_0^2 - \tfrac{1}{2}(\mu_1 c_1 + \mu_2 c_2)q_0 - \tfrac{1}{4}\mu_1\mu_2 c_1 c_2 < 0.$$

But the discriminant of this quadratic q_0 is zero and hence the inequality can never be satisfied.

§3. Reduction of an Indirect Control to a Special Direct Control

Take the initial basic system (II, 2.1) of indirect control and introduce new $(n + 1)$ vectors

$$z = \begin{pmatrix} x \\ \xi \end{pmatrix}, \qquad -b_0 = \begin{pmatrix} 0 \\ \cdot \\ \cdot \\ \cdot \\ 0 \\ 1 \end{pmatrix}, \qquad c_0 = \begin{pmatrix} c \\ -\rho \end{pmatrix}.$$

Define also an $(n \times 1) \times (n + 1)$ matrix A_0 to take the place of A as

$$A_0 = \begin{pmatrix} A & -b \\ 0 & 0 \end{pmatrix}.$$

Then (II, 2.1) is equivalent to the system

(3.1)
$$\dot{z} = A_0 z - \varphi(\sigma)b_0$$

$$\sigma = c_0' z$$

which is of the direct control type but with the peculiarity that the matrix A_0 is not stable since it has one characteristic root zero. The order of the new system is $n + 1$.

§4. Linearization of Direct Controls

Since $\mu\sigma$, $\mu > 0$, is an admissible φ function, its substitution for φ in a control equation gives rise to a linear system. In order to have absolute stability this linear system must be asymptotically stable. From this there will arise certain absolute stability conditions. It may be said that this question has been fully investigated by Yacubovich notably in references [2] and [4].

The linearization problem is closely related to the well-known *problem of Aizerman*. The latter author inquired essentially into the extent to which one could substitute for a function φ restricted by

$$\alpha\sigma^2 < \sigma\varphi(\sigma) < \beta\sigma^2$$

a linear function $\mu\sigma$, $\alpha < \mu < \beta$. Ample details and references on this problem will be found in Pliss [1].

Take first the direct control (1.1). The linearized system is

(4.1)
$$\dot{x} = (A - \mu bc')x.$$

A n.a.s.c. to have (4.1) asymptotically stable is that the matrix $A - \mu bc'$ be stable, i.e., that its characteristic roots have negative real parts. The characteristic equation of this matrix is $|zE - A + \mu bc'| = 0$. It is convenient to write $zE - A = A_z$ so that $|A_z| = 0$ is the characteristic

43

equation of A itself. The above relation is then

(4.2) $$|A_z + \mu bc'| = 0.$$

As in (II, §2) one shows that absolute stability does impose the condition that A possess no characteristic roots with positive real parts. This does not exclude that A possess characteristic roots with zero real parts: zero or pure imaginary.

Let it be assumed then that A is semistable or stable and examine more closely the characteristic equation (4.2). We are concerned with μ small and briefly assume that z is not a characteristic root of A so that A_z^{-1} exists. Then (4.2) is equivalent to $|E + \mu bc'A_z^{-1}| = 0$. A closer look at this last expression will yield a simpler expression for (4.2).

Consider the characteristic roots of the $n \times n$ matrix pq' where p and q are n vectors. Since each row of pq' is a multiple of the row vector q' the matrix has rank one and hence one nonzero characteristic root. Since the trace of a matrix is the sum of its characteristic roots it follows that the one nonzero characteristic root of pq' is trace pq'. But trace $pq' = q'p$ and so $|zE - pq'| = z^{n-1}(z - q'p)$. This reduces to $|E - pq'| = (1 - q'p)$ by setting $z = 1$. For $q' = c'A_z^{-1}$ and $p = -\mu b$, (4.2) becomes

(4.2a) $$|A_z| \cdot (1 + \mu c'A_z^{-1}b) = 0.$$

The solutions $z(\mu)$ of (4.2a) for μ small are very near to, but not identical with, the characteristic roots of A. Since A is semistable some are then very near to zero or to some points on the complex axis. We first investigate $z(\mu)$ which $\to 0$ with μ. Since for such a solution $|A_z| \neq 0$, it satisfies the relation

(4.3) $$\frac{-1}{\mu} = c'A_z^{-1}b.$$

Let zero be a root of order k of $|A_z| = 0$, and so a pole of order at most k of $c'A_z^{-1}b$. Thus near zero

$$c'A_z^{-1}b = \frac{\alpha}{z^k} + \frac{\beta}{z^{k-1}} + \cdots + \gamma + \delta z + \cdots.$$

The coefficients α, β,... are all real for they are merely the coefficients of the McLaurin expansion of $z^k c'A_z^{-1}b$. Moreover $\alpha \neq 0$ since otherwise (4.2) would have the fixed solution $z(\mu) = 0$ and (4.1) would not

44

be asymptotically stable for $\mu > 0$ and small. Thus zero is actually a pole of order k of $c'A_z^{-1}b$.

From the above series expansion there follows in succession

$$c'A_z^{-1}b = \frac{\alpha}{z^k}\left(1 + \frac{\beta}{\alpha}z + \cdots\right),$$

$$\frac{-1}{\alpha\mu} = \frac{1}{z^k}\left(1 + \frac{\beta}{\alpha}z + \cdots\right),$$

$$z^k\left(1 - \frac{\beta}{\alpha}z + \cdots\right) = -\alpha\mu.$$

Hence setting $\mu = v^k$, $v > 0$, one finds

$$z\left(1 - \frac{\beta}{k\alpha}z + \cdots\right) = (-\alpha)^{1/k}v.$$

By the implicit function theorem this yields for v small

(4.4) $$z = (-\alpha)^{1/k}v + \frac{\beta}{k\alpha}(-\alpha)^{2/k}v^2 + \cdots.$$

This expression provides k determinations of $z(\mu)$ for μ small which are very near to the vertices of a regular polygon centered at the origin. Hence if $k > 2$ some determination will fall to the right of the imaginary axis thus contradicting the assumption that the linearized system is asymptotically stable. Therefore one requires that $k \leq 2$, i.e. $k = 0, 1, 2$. The value $k = 0$ offers no interest; no characteristic root comes near zero for μ small. There remains $k = 1$ or 2 and we examine these values separately.

Let first $k = 1$. Then from (4.4)

$$z = -\alpha v + \cdots$$

which must be to the left of the imaginary axis. This requires that $\alpha > 0$.

Take now $k = 2$. This time

$$z = (-\alpha)^{1/2}v - \frac{\beta}{k}v^2 + \cdots.$$

If $\alpha < 0$ one of the solutions will fall to the right of the imaginary axis.

Hence one must have $\alpha > 0$. As a consequence

$$z = i\sqrt{\alpha} \cdot v - \frac{\beta}{\alpha}v^2 + \cdots,$$

$$\mathrm{Re}\, z = \frac{-\beta}{k}v^2 + \cdots.$$

Thus to have z fall to the left of the complex axis for $\mu > 0$ and small, one must have $\beta \geqq 0$. To sum up *when zero is a double characteristic root of A necessary absolute stability conditions for the system* (1.1) *are* $\alpha > 0$, $\beta \geqq 0$.

Quite similarly one may obtain the following results for absolute stability and a complex characteristic root $i\omega$:

(a) $i\omega$ *may have at most multiplicity two.*

(b) *If $i\omega$ is simple and in its vicinity*

$$c'A_z^{-1}b = \frac{\alpha}{z - i\omega} + \beta + \gamma(z - i\omega) + \cdots$$

then $\mathrm{Re}\,\alpha \geqq 0$.

(c) *If $i\omega$ is double and in its vicinity*

$$c'A_z^{-1}b = \frac{\alpha}{(z - i\omega)^2} + \frac{\beta}{(z - i\omega)} + \gamma + \delta(z - i\omega) + \cdots,$$

then $\alpha > 0$, $\mathrm{Re}\,\beta \geqq 0$.

§5. Linearization of Indirect Controls

The linearized system (II, 2.3) is

$$(5.1)\qquad \begin{aligned} \dot{y} &= Ay - \mu\sigma b \\[1mm] \dot{\sigma} &= c'y - \rho\mu\sigma \end{aligned}$$

with characteristic equation

$$\begin{vmatrix} A_z & \mu b \\ -c' & z + \rho\mu \end{vmatrix} = 0.$$

As before it is equivalent to

$$(5.2)\qquad 1 + \mu\,\frac{\rho + c'A_z^{-1}b}{z} = 1 + \mu g(z) = 0.$$

If one considers (5.1) as a direct control then $g(z)$ plays the role of the expression $c'A_z^{-1}b$. In terms of the present A_z we have: *zero is at most a simple, and $i\omega$, $\omega \neq 0$, at most a double characteristic root of A*.

The special property of the zero root is caused by the fact that $z = 0$ is already a pole of $g(z)$. The detailed analysis follows.

(a) *Zero is not a characteristic root of A.* Then near $z = 0$

$$g(z) = \frac{\alpha}{z} + \beta + \gamma z + \cdots$$

where $\alpha = \rho + c'A_0^{-1}b$. Now $A_0 = -A$ and the calculation of A_0^{-1} yields at once $A_0^{-1} = -A^{-1}$. Hence, referring to §4 one must have $\alpha > 0$ which yields

$$\rho > c'A^{-1}b,$$

an inequality already obtained by another method in (III, §2).

(b) *Zero is a simple characteristic root of A.* Let then

$$c'A_z^{-1}b = \frac{\alpha}{z} + \beta + \gamma z + \cdots.$$

As a consequence

$$g(z) = \frac{\alpha}{z^2} + \frac{\beta + \rho}{z} + \gamma + \cdots$$

and from §4 one obtains the conditions

$$\alpha > 0, \qquad \beta \geqq -\rho.$$

(c) *$i\omega(\omega \neq 0)$ is a simple characteristic root of A.* Here then

$$c'A_z^{-1}b = \frac{\alpha}{z - i\omega} + \beta + \cdots.$$

Hence

$$g(z) = \frac{\alpha}{i\omega(z - i\omega)} + \frac{\beta}{i\omega} + \cdots.$$

Hence from (§4),

$$\operatorname{Im}\frac{\alpha}{\omega} > 0.$$

(d) $i\omega(\omega \neq 0)$ *is a double characteristic root of A.* This time

$$c'A_z^{-1}b = \frac{\alpha}{(z - i\omega)^2} + \frac{\beta}{(z - i\omega)} + \gamma + \cdots$$

$$g(z) = \frac{\alpha}{i\omega(z - i\omega)^2} + \frac{\beta}{i\omega(z - i\omega)} + \cdots$$

and so from §4

$$\operatorname{Im} \frac{\alpha}{\omega} < 0, \qquad \operatorname{Im} \frac{\beta}{i\omega} \leqq 0.$$

§6. Direct Control with Matrices B or C of Rank $< n$

Absolute stability has rested in §1 upon matrices B, $C > 0$. Still preserving the form of the Liapunov function V of §1, it is of interest to discuss to what extent one may be able to reach the desirable goal of absolute stability with critical matrices B or C. Recall these two properties (IX, §3):

(6.1) *If A is stable and $C > 0$ then $B > 0$.*

(6.2) *If B and $C > 0$ then A is stable.*

Observe now that if $c = 0$ then the system (1.1) is uncontrolled. As this is without interest we may assume that $c \neq 0$. Hence one may select the coordinates such that $c'x = x_n = \sigma$. This suggests the following convention: If F is an $n \times n$ matrix or f an n vector, denote by F_0 or f_0 the result of deleting the last row and column from F and the last component from f. In particular write

$$A = \begin{vmatrix} A_0 & f \\ g' & \alpha \end{vmatrix}, \qquad B = \begin{vmatrix} B_0 & h \\ h' & \beta \end{vmatrix}, \qquad C = \begin{vmatrix} C_0 & k \\ k' & \gamma \end{vmatrix}.$$

Here f, g, h are $(n - 1)$ vectors and α, β, γ are scalars. With these designations and coordinates the system (1.1) assumes the form

(6.3)
$$\dot{x}_0 = A_0 x_0 + f\sigma - b_0 \varphi(\sigma)$$

$$\dot{\sigma} = g'x_0 + \alpha\sigma - \rho\varphi(\sigma).$$

§6. DIRECT CONTROL WITH MATRICES B OR C OF RANK $<n$

The case of particular interest is that of B of rank $<n$. Our goal continues to be V positive definite for all x and all admissible φ. Hence

$$V(x_0, 0) = x_0'B_0x_0$$

must be positive definite and so $B_0 > 0$. Thus B is of rank $n - 1$ and this is assumed henceforth.

Since we wish to have $V > 0$ for all admissible φ, this must happen for $\varphi = 2\mu\sigma$, $\mu > 0$. Thus the quadratic form in x_0, σ

(6.4) $$x_0'B_0x_0 + 2h'x_0\sigma + (\beta + \mu)\sigma^2$$

must be positive definite for all $\mu > 0$. Since $B_0 > 0$ the only additional Sylvester condition is

$$\begin{vmatrix} B_0 & h \\ h' & \beta + \mu \end{vmatrix} > 0,$$

or, according to (IX, §2)

(6.5) $$(\beta + \mu) > h'B_0^{-1}h.$$

Now

$$\beta > h'B_0^{-1}h$$

implies that $B > 0$ and so it is excluded. If

$$\beta = h'B_0^{-1}h$$

then

$$x'Bx = (x_0' + h'B_0^{-1}\sigma)B_0(x_0 + hB_0^{-1}\sigma) + \mu\sigma^2.$$

Hence if one chooses as coordinates $(x_0 + hB_0^{-1}\sigma, \sigma)$ our situation will be unchanged save that with the new coordinates $\beta = 0$. This is assumed henceforth. As a consequence (6.5) becomes

$$\mu > h'B_0^{-1}h.$$

Since this must hold for μ arbitrarily small positive and $B_0 > 0$, necessarily $h = 0$. Thus under our stringent conditions we have $B = \text{diag}(B_0, 0)$.

Upon taking into account the properties of the admissible class φ it is easily verified that V fulfills all its expected requirements regarding absolute stability.

49

The situation regarding $-\dot{V}$ is less simple. There are again the relations (1.5) and (1.6). One faces then two alternatives: (a) as in §1 obtaining absolute stability through A stable, $C > 0$, the relation (1.9) and $-\dot{V}$ a positive semidefinite quadratic form in x and φ; (b) accept that A may be unstable, preserve $B_0 > 0$ and look for $-\dot{V}(x_0, \sigma)$ a positive definite function of x_0, σ. Since then $-\dot{V}(x_0, 0) = x_0'C_0x_0 > 0$ for $x_0 \neq 0$, one will have $C_0 > 0$. We do not return to (a) and in the next section discuss B, C both of rank $n - 1$.

Coupled with our desire to have $V(x_0, \sigma)$ and $-\dot{V}(x_0, \sigma)$ positive definite this is equivalent to $B_0, C_0 > 0$.

§7. Direct Controls with Matrices B, C, of Rank $n - 1$

As just observed this is equivalent to $B_0, C_0 > 0$. As in §6 let the coordinates be so chosen that $B = \mathrm{diag}(B_0, 0)$. Now from the Liapunov relation for A, B, C there follows

(7.1)
$$\begin{vmatrix} A_0'B_0 + B_0A_0 & B_0 f \\ f'B_0 & 0 \end{vmatrix} = - \begin{vmatrix} C_0 & k \\ k' & \gamma \end{vmatrix}.$$

Hence

(7.2) $\qquad A_0'B_0 + B_0A_0 = -C_0, \qquad k = -B_0 f, \qquad \gamma = 0.$

Now the determinant of the quadratic form $x'Cx$ must be zero, as rank $C = n - 1$. Hence

$$\begin{vmatrix} C_0 & k \\ k' & 0 \end{vmatrix} = 0.$$

Since $C_0 > 0$ and referring to (IX, §2) this yields $k'C_0^{-1}k = 0$. Since C_0^{-1} is likewise > 0 necessarily $k = 0$, hence also $f = B_0^{-1}k = 0$. Thus

$$C = \mathrm{diag}(C_0, 0),$$

and (6.3) looks like this:

(7.3)
$$\dot{x}_0 = A_0x_0 - b_0\varphi(\sigma)$$
$$\dot{\sigma} = g'x_0 + \alpha\sigma - \rho\varphi(\sigma).$$

Note that α is now a real characteristic root of A. Hence $\alpha \leqq 0$. Moreover from (6.2) and (7.2) there follows that A_0 is stable and so if $\alpha < 0$, A itself is stable. The system (7.3) is then a standard direct control of the type of (1.1).

Suppose that $\alpha = 0$. Then the system (7.3) may be identified with (II, 2.3) if $\rho \neq 0$: an indirect control, or with (1.1) if $\rho = 0$: direct control, both of dimension $n - 1$ and basic matrix A_0. In the first case A, b, c, y of (II, 2.3) correspond here to A_0, b_0, g, x while in the second A, b, c of (1.1) correspond to $A_0, b_0, A_0^{-1}g_0$. Both cases are covered by our earlier arguments.

Suppose now $\alpha \neq 0$. With V as before we can calculate $\dot{V}$ simply by observing that it is the sum of its value for $\alpha = 0$ plus α times the coefficient of α. Hence:

$$-\dot{V} = \{x_0'B_0x_0 + 2d_0'x_0\varphi(\sigma) + \rho\varphi^2(\sigma)\} - 2\alpha\sigma\varphi(\sigma), \qquad d_0 = B_0b_0 - \tfrac{1}{2}g.$$

Since $\alpha \leq 0$, and $\sigma\varphi(\sigma) > 0$ for $\sigma \neq 0$, in order to have $-\dot{V}$ positive definite as a function of x_0, σ it is sufficient that the quadratic form in x_0, φ in the bracket be

positive definite if $\alpha = 0$
positive semidefinite if $\alpha < 0$.

Hence the final condition

$$(7.4) \qquad \left. \begin{array}{c} \rho > \\[4pt] \rho \gtreqqless \end{array} \right\} \; \left\{ d_0'C_0^{-1}d_0 \quad \text{for} \right\} \; \begin{array}{c} \alpha = 0 \\[4pt] \alpha < 0. \end{array}$$

When (7.4) holds we will have $-\dot{V}$ positive definite in x_0, σ, that is, in x and this for all admissible φ. Since $V \to \infty$ with $\|x\|$, absolute stability will have been achieved in both cases.

The preceding discussion leads to the following result:

(7.5) *Let both B, C be of rank $n - 1$. Then n.a.s.c. to have V and $-\dot{V}$ both positive definite as functions of x or x_0, φ, are that in appropriate coordinates $B = \mathrm{diag}(B_0, 0)$, $C = \mathrm{diag}(C_0, 0)$ with $B_0, C_0 > 0$ (hence A_0 stable) plus the property (7.4). When this holds the system (1.1) is absolutely stable.*

§8. Direct Control Whose Matrix A Has Zero as a Characteristic Root (Kenneth Meyer)

In this section and the next we fully discuss several critical direct controls. In the first case the matrix of the linear part of the system has

51

a simple zero characteristic root. By a suitable change of coordinates the system is then

$$\dot{x} = Ax - b\varphi(\sigma)$$

(8.1)
$$\dot{\xi} = \beta\varphi(\sigma)$$

$$\sigma = c'x - \gamma\xi$$

where x, b and c are n vectors; ξ, β, γ are scalars and A is an $n \times n$ stable matrix. Now $\beta = 0$ implies that $\xi = $ constant and therefore $\xi = 0$ to achieve stability. Hence the system is just (1.1). We may therefore assume $\beta \neq 0$. Then replacing ξ by ξ/β we have

$$\dot{x} = Ax - b\varphi(\sigma)$$

(8.2)
$$\dot{\xi} = \varphi(\sigma)$$

$$\sigma = c'x - \gamma\xi.$$

This is a special form of an indirect control of dimension n with control variables ξ, σ. Its reduction to the natural indirect control of (II, 2.1) will be established in (VII, §1) (Popov system). There is no need therefore to discuss this system any further.

Let us turn our attention then to the more interesting case of a double zero root. It will be convenient to take the system as $n + 2$ dimensional. If $A_0,...$ denotes the usual quantities $A,...$ in the system (1.1) then by a suitable choice of coordinates $A_0 = \operatorname{diag}(O_2, A)$ where A is an $n \times n$ stable matrix and O_2 has one of two forms

$$O_2 = \begin{pmatrix} 0 & 0 \\ 0 & 0 \end{pmatrix} \quad \text{or} \quad O_2 = \begin{pmatrix} 0 & 0 \\ 1 & 0 \end{pmatrix}.$$

If O_2 is of the first form the system reduces to

$$\dot{\xi}_1 = -\beta_1\varphi(\sigma)$$

$$\dot{\xi}_2 = -\beta_2\varphi(\sigma)$$

$$\dot{x} = Ax - b\varphi(\sigma)$$

$$\sigma = \gamma_1\xi_1 + \gamma_2\xi_2 + c'x$$

It is clear though that there exist nonzero constants $\bar{\xi}_1$ and $\bar{\xi}_2$ such that the above system has the solution $\xi_1 = \bar{\xi}_1, \xi_2 = \bar{\xi}_2, x = 0, \sigma = 0$.

52

Thus this direct control cannot be stabilized when O_2 is of the first form. In the second case the system reduces to

$$\dot{\xi}_1 = \qquad - \beta_1 \varphi(\sigma)$$
$$\dot{\xi}_2 = \xi_1 - \beta_2 \varphi(\sigma)$$
(8.3)
$$\dot{x} = Ax - b\varphi(\sigma)$$
$$\sigma = \gamma_1 \xi_1 + \gamma_2 \xi_2 + c'x.$$

Now choose as a Liapunov function for (8.3)

$$V = \alpha \xi_1^2 + x'Bx + \Phi(\sigma)$$

where α will be chosen later so that $\alpha > 0$. In this case

$$B_0 = \text{diag}(\alpha, 0, B)$$

and from the Liapunov relation

$$A_0'B_0 + B_0 A_0 = - C_0$$

one finds

$$C_0 = \text{diag}(0, 0, C), \qquad - C = A'B + BA.$$

Also

$$d_0' = (B_0 b_0 - \tfrac{1}{2} A_0' c_0)' = (\{\alpha \beta_1 - \tfrac{1}{2} \gamma_2\}, 0, d)$$
$$d = Bb - \tfrac{1}{2} A'c$$
$$c_0' b_0 = \beta_1 \gamma_1 + \beta_2 \gamma_2 + c'b.$$

Hence

$$- \dot{V} = x_0' C_0 x_0 + 2 d_0' x_0 \varphi + c_0' b_0 \varphi^2$$
$$= x'Cx + (\alpha \beta_1 - \gamma_2) \xi_1 \varphi + 2 d' x \varphi$$
$$+ (\beta_1 \gamma_1 + \beta_2 \gamma_2 + c'b) \varphi^2.$$

Let us suppose that there exists an $\alpha > 0$ such that

$$\alpha \beta_1 - \tfrac{1}{2} \gamma_2 = 0$$

or what is equivalent

(8.4)
$$\beta_1 \gamma_2 > 0.$$

Then we can choose $C > 0$ and thus $B > 0$. Note now that B_0 is not positive definite in ξ_1, ξ_2 and x but only positive definite in ξ_1 and x.

53

Since $\gamma_2 \neq 0$ (8.4) the term $\Phi(\sigma)$ makes V positive definite in ξ_1, ξ_2, x and moreover $V \rightarrow \infty$ as $\|x\| + |\xi_1| + |\xi_2| \rightarrow \infty$.

We cannot achieve as much for $-\dot{V}$. Let us, however, endeavor to make it a positive definite quadratic form in x and φ. This merely requires the inequality (F_d) or

$$(8.5) \qquad \beta_1 \gamma_1 + \beta_2 \gamma_2 + c'b > d'C^{-1}d.$$

This only guarantees that $-\dot{V} \geq 0$ in the space of ξ_1, ξ_2, x, σ but $-\dot{V} > 0$ in the space x, σ. At this point we have recourse to the theorem of LaSalle (IX, 4.8).

In our case $\dot{V} = 0$ if, and only if, $x = 0$, $\sigma = 0$. This implies that if a solution of (8.3) is to remain in the set where $\dot{V} = 0$ it must satisfy

$$\dot{\xi}_1 = 0, \qquad \dot{\xi}_2 = \xi_1, \qquad 0 = \gamma_1 \xi_1 + \gamma_2 \xi_2.$$

But the general solution to the above equation is $\xi_1 = \delta_1$, $\xi_2 = \delta_1 t + \delta_2$, $0 = \gamma_1 \delta_1 + \gamma_2 (\delta_1 t + \delta_2)$ where δ_1 and δ_2 are arbitrary constants. Since $\gamma_2 \neq 0$ this implies that $\delta_1 = \delta_2 = 0$. Thus the LaSalle conditions are satisfied and so absolute stability has been established under the condition $C > 0$, (8.4) and (8.5).

It will be of some interest to compare the above conditions with the necessary conditions found in §4. The function $c'A_z^{-1}b$ found in §4 is now

$$(\gamma_1, \gamma_2) \begin{pmatrix} z & 0 \\ -1 & z \end{pmatrix}^{-1} \begin{pmatrix} \beta_1 \\ \beta_2 \end{pmatrix} + c'A_z^{-1}b$$

$$= \frac{\beta_1 \gamma_2}{z^2} + \frac{\beta_1 \gamma_1 + \beta_2 \gamma_2}{z} + \cdots.$$

Thus we see that the conditions found in §4 are simply $\beta_1 \gamma_2 > 0$ and $\beta_1 \gamma_1 + \beta_2 \gamma_2 \geq 0$, and are compatible with (8.4) and (8.5).

Indirect control whose matrix has zero as simple characteristic root. In accordance with the scheme of §3, this case may be identified with the one just considered. The indirect control is of dimension $n + 1$ and has for "state" matrix $\mathrm{diag}(A, 0)$ the state variables being x and ξ_2. The preceding treatment: case O_2 may thus be directly applied here.

§9. Direct Control Whose Matrix Has a Pair of Conjugate Pure Imaginary Characteristic Roots (Kenneth Meyer)

It is again convenient to take a system of dimension $n + 2$. In suitable coordinates the system will be represented by

$$\dot{\xi} = i\omega\xi - \beta\varphi(\sigma)$$

$$\dot{\bar{\xi}} = -i\omega\bar{\xi} - \bar{\beta}\varphi(\sigma)$$

(9.1)

$$\dot{x} = Ax - b\varphi(\sigma)$$

$$\sigma = \gamma\xi + \bar{\gamma}\bar{\xi} + c'x$$

where the Greek letters are scalars with $\omega > 0$; x, b and c are n vectors and A is a real stable $n \times n$ matrix. Let $A_0,...$ be as in the previous section. Thus

$$A_0 = \text{diag}(i\omega, -i\omega, A), \qquad b_0' = (\beta, \bar{\beta}, b'), \qquad c_0' = (\gamma, \bar{\gamma}, c').$$

Choose as a Liapunov function

$$V = 2\alpha\xi\bar{\xi} + x'Bx + \Phi(\sigma)$$

where α will be specified in a moment and α will be positive. Here then

$$B_0 = \text{diag}(\alpha, \alpha, B).$$

From the Liapunov relation

$$A_0^*B_0 + B_0A_0 = -C_0$$

one finds at once

$$C_0 = \text{diag}(0, 0, C), \qquad -C = A'B + BA,$$

and also

$$d_0' = (B_0b_0 - \tfrac{1}{2}A_0'c_0)' = (\alpha\bar{\beta} - \tfrac{1}{2}i\omega\gamma, \alpha\beta + \tfrac{1}{2}i\omega\bar{\gamma}, d)'$$

$$d = Bb - \tfrac{1}{2}A'c$$

$$c_0'b_0 = \beta\gamma + \bar{\beta}\bar{\gamma} + c'b.$$

55

Hence

$$-\dot{V} = x_0'C_0 x_0 + 2d_0'x_0\varphi + c_0'b_0\varphi^2$$
$$= x'Cx + 2((\alpha\bar{\beta} - \tfrac{1}{2}i\omega\gamma)\xi + (\alpha\beta + \tfrac{1}{2}i\omega\bar{\gamma})\bar{\xi} + d'x)\varphi$$
$$+ (\beta\gamma + \bar{\beta}\bar{\gamma} + c'b)\varphi^2.$$

Let us assume that there is a positive α such that $(\alpha\bar{\beta} - \tfrac{1}{2}i\omega\gamma) = 0$ or what is equivalent

$$(9.2) \qquad\qquad \operatorname{Re}\gamma\beta = 0, \qquad \operatorname{Im}\gamma\beta < 0.$$

These conditions may clearly be satisfied. We also choose $C > 0$ hence also $B > 0$, and as a consequence V is positive definite in $x, \xi, \bar{\xi}, \sigma$ for every admissible φ and moreover $V \to \infty$ with $\|x\| + |\xi| + |\sigma|$.

Aiming again toward the theorem of LaSalle we require $-\dot{V}$ to be positive definite in x and φ. This merely requires here

$$(9.3) \qquad\qquad \beta\gamma + \bar{\beta}\bar{\gamma} + c'b > d'C^{-1}d.$$

Under the condition (9.3) $-V$ is a positive definite quadratic form in x and φ. Thus $-V = 0$ if, and only if, $x = 0$, $\sigma = 0$. Thus if a solution of (9.1) is to remain in the set where $\dot{V} = 0$ it must satisfy the equations

$$\dot{\xi} = i\omega\xi, \qquad \dot{\bar{\xi}} = -i\omega\bar{\xi}, \qquad \gamma\xi + \gamma\bar{\xi} = 0$$

That is, there must exist a constant δ such that

$$\gamma\delta e^{i\omega t} + \bar{\gamma}\bar{\delta}e^{-i\omega t} = 0.$$

Since the two exponentials are linearly independent $\gamma\delta = 0$ and since $\gamma \neq 0$, $\delta = 0$. Thus LaSalle's conditions are satisfied and absolute stability is assured by $C > 0$, (9.2) and (9.3).

§10. Multiple Feedbacks

In various practical situations one may have a control depending on several parameters. This case has already been dealt with by Letov [1, Chapter IV] and Popov [4].

To conform with our general notations designate

$$\left.\begin{array}{c}\text{the analog}\\ \text{of}\\ \text{the scalar}\end{array}\right\}\begin{array}{c}\sigma\\ \xi\\ \varphi(\sigma)\end{array}\qquad \begin{array}{c}\text{by the}\\ r \text{ vector}\end{array}\qquad \left\{\begin{array}{c}v\\ u\\ f(v).\end{array}\right.$$

By analogy with the earlier situation, the following conditions are imposed upon the vector function $f(v)$:

   I. $f(v)$ is continuous;

   II. $f_h(v) \cdot v_h > 0$ if $v_h \neq 0$, and $f_h(v) = 0$ if $v_h = 0$;

  III. the integral $\int f(v) \, dv$ along any ray from the origin $v = 0$ is divergent.

This last condition plays the same role as its analog: to make all solutions tend to the origin as $t \to +\infty$.

An example of a function such as $f(v)$ (but not the only example) is one in which every $f_h = f_h(v_h)$ (scalar function) where f_h satisfies the conditions of I, namely,

   I. $f_h(v_h)$ is continuous for all v_h;

   II. $v_h f_h(v_h) > 0$ for $v_h \neq 0$; $f_h(0) = 0$;

  III. $\int^{+\infty} f_h(v_h) \, dv_h$ is divergent.

However, for instance $\|v\| f(v)$, ($f(v)$ as just defined), is likewise a function of the general class. We have now the possibility of associating this new situation with indirect and direct controls.

Indirect control. The system will be

$$\dot{x} = Ax + Gu$$

(10.1)
$$\dot{u} = f(v)$$

$$v = Hx + Ru,$$

where A is our usual stable $n \times n$ matrix and G, H, R are constant $n \times r$, $r \times n$ and $r \times r$ matrices.

We proceed in full analogy with the earlier case. In the first place the origin will be the only critical point if, and only if, the determinant

(10.2)
$$\begin{vmatrix} A & G \\ H & R \end{vmatrix} \neq 0.$$

This is assumed henceforth. We are then justified in applying the change of coordinates $(x, u) \rightarrow (y, v)$ defined by $y = Ax + Gu$, $v = Hx + Ru$. The new system is

(10.3)
$$\dot{y} = Ay + Gf(v)$$

$$\dot{v} = Hy + Rf(v).$$

The goal is still to make the system absolutely stable: asymptotically stable in the large and regardless of the choice of the function $f(v)$ within its class. The same theorem of Liapunov, with Barbashin-Krassovskii complement is to be applied. First define

$$\Phi(v) = \int_0^v f(v) \cdot dv$$

where the integral is taken along the ray L from the origin to the point v. That is, if, say s is a parameter along the ray, with value s at v then

$$\Phi(v) = \int_0^s f(v(s)) \cdot \frac{dv}{ds} \cdot ds.$$

Since $f_h(v)$ always has the sign of v_h (except that $f_h = 0$ for $v_h = 0$) we see that $\Phi(v)$, for $v \neq 0$, is a sum of positive terms if $v \neq 0$, and only zero for $v = 0$. Thus $\Phi(v) > 0$ for every $v \neq 0$. It is, of course, continuous in v, and $\rightarrow + \infty$ with $\|v\|$ as the latter $\rightarrow \infty$.

Choose now

(10.4)
$$V(y, v) = y'By + \Phi(v)$$

where B is selected as before: one takes an arbitrary $n \times n$ matrix $C > 0$ and defines B as the unique solution of Liapunov's equation

$$A'B + BA = -C.$$

One finds now

(10.5)
$$-\dot{V}(y, v) = y'Cy - f'(v)Rf(v) - f'(v)Ky - y'Kf$$

$$K = G'B + \tfrac{1}{2}H.$$

In writing this relation we have utilized the property that since $f'Hy = y'Hf$, we have

$$f'Hy = \tfrac{1}{2}(f'Hy + y'Hf).$$

58

Since $f'Rf = f'R'f$, we observe at all events that the positive definiteness of $-\dot{V}$ implies that of $-f'Rf = -f'(\frac{1}{2}(R + R'))f$, and hence that

$$(10.6) \qquad\qquad R + R' < 0.$$

Basically, however, the positive definiteness of $-\dot{V}$ is equivalent to the classical Hurwitz conditions for the positive definiteness of the quadratic form in (10.5) in the variables y, f. If we set $K = (k_{ij})$, $R = (r_{ij})$ and define

$$K_s = (k_{ij}); \qquad R_s = (r_{ij}); \qquad i,j \leq s,$$

$$\Delta_s = \begin{vmatrix} C & -K_s \\ -K_s' & -R_s \end{vmatrix},$$

then the Sylvester conditions not yet fulfilled are

$$(10.7) \qquad\qquad \Delta_1 > 0, \quad \Delta_2 > 0,..., \Delta_r > 0.$$

These are the conditions which correspond to the unique inequality (F_i) for $r = 1$. Of course, the inequalities (10.7) imply (10.6). Indeed if one reverses the orders of the variables from y, f to f, y one obtains, from Sylvester's inequalities, as first conditions for the positive definiteness of $-\dot{V}$ those which express that $f'(\frac{1}{2}(R + R'))f$ is positive definite.

Direct control. This time the system is

$$\dot{x} = Ax + Gu$$

$$u = f(v)$$

$$v = Hx,$$

or with u eliminated

$$(10.8) \qquad \begin{aligned} \dot{x} &= Ax + Gf(v) \\ v &= Hx. \end{aligned}$$

It may also be written as a single vector equation

$$\dot{x} = Ax + Gf(Hx).$$

The origin will be the only critical point provided that, as assumed henceforth, $Ax + Gf(Hx) = 0$ has $x = 0$ as its sole solution.

One may conveniently complete (10.8) with

$$\dot{v} = H\dot{x} = HAx + HG(v)$$

or setting $HA = H_0, HG = R_0$, by

$$\dot{v} = H_0 x + R_0 f(v).$$

Take now as before

$$V(x) = x'Bx + \Phi(v).$$

With B, C related as before, one obtains

$$-\dot{V}(x) = x'Cx - f'(v)R_0 f(v) - f'K_0 x - x'K_0 f$$

$$K_0 = G'B + \tfrac{1}{2}H_0.$$

Set now

$$K_0 = (k_{ij}^0); \qquad R_0 = (r_{ij}^0);$$

$$K_s{}^0 = (k_{ij}^0); \qquad K_s{}^0 = (k_{ij});$$

$$R_s{}^0 = (r_{ij}^0); \qquad i, j \leqq s;$$

$$\Delta_s{}^0 = \begin{vmatrix} C & -K_s{}^0 \\ -K_s{}^{0'} & -R_s \end{vmatrix}.$$

The difficulty found in §1 occurs here also. It is settled again by reference to LaSalle's theorem (IX, 4.8) and the sufficient conditions for absolute stability are

$$\Delta_1 = 0, \quad \Delta_2 = 0,..., \Delta_r = 0.$$

Chapter 5

SYSTEMS REPRESENTED BY A SET OF EQUATIONS OF HIGHER ORDER

In practice one has often to deal with fundamental systems composed of several equations of any order. In theory this offers no novelty since by introducing more variables such a system may be reduced to the standard type of a number of equations of order unity. Practically however it is decidedly advantageous to be able to deal with these systems as one finds them and not after a more or less artificial reduction to another type. Our purpose in the present chapter is to examine some of the problems without undue change of type. This does not mean, of course, that we forego the theoretical convenience of the reduction to the standard set of equations of order one, but only that we will endeavor as much as possible to deal with the equations as they stand.

§1. Generalities

The variety of the systems that may arise is virtually endless. For the sake of orientation we discuss rapidly a fundamental system consisting of a single equation of order n with constant coefficients:

$$(1.1) \qquad \eta^{(n)} + \alpha_1 \eta^{(n-1)} + \cdots + \alpha_n \eta = 0.$$

Introduce the new variables $x_1, x_2,..., x_n$ components of a vector x, and defined by $x_1 = \eta, x_2 = \dot{\eta},..., x_n = \eta^{(n-1)}$. As a consequence the unique equation (1.1) becomes equivalent to the system

$$\dot{x}_1 = x_2, \quad \dot{x}_2 = x_3,..., \dot{x}_{n-1} = x_n$$

(1.2)

$$\dot{x}_n = -\alpha_1 x_n - \alpha_2 x_{n-1} - \cdots - \alpha_n x_1$$

with coefficient matrix

$$A = \begin{pmatrix} 0 & 1 & & & & 0 \\ 0 & 0 & 1 & & & 0 \\ & \cdot & \cdot & \cdot & \cdot & \cdot & \cdot \\ & \cdot & \cdot & \cdot & \cdot & \cdot & \cdot \\ & & & & 0 & 1 \\ -\alpha_n & \cdot & \cdot & \cdot & \cdot & -\alpha_2, & -\alpha_1 \end{pmatrix}$$

The characteristic equation is

(1.3) $$|rE - A| = r^n + \alpha_1 r^{n-1} + \cdots + \alpha_n = 0.$$

As before A is assumed to be stable.

Part of our problem is that we will have to deal directly with the matrix A, that is with the coordinates x, since they have a particular significance for the problem under consideration. Or more accurately, one will be free to change coordinates provided that the system (1.2) retains its form and the matrix A is unchanged. This will become clear in a moment.

This is as good a place as any to make a few rapid observations regarding linear systems. After that we turn our attention to indirect, then to direct controls.

§2. A Digression on Linear Systems

There has been developed around linear systems a widely used technique based upon the simple and well-known device of designating time differentiation by an operator, usually D. Thus $\dot{x}$ is written Dx, $\ddot{x}$ is written D^2x, etc. As an example the standard indirect control system assumes the form

$$(D - A)x = -\xi b$$

$$D\sigma = \varphi(\sigma)$$

$$\sigma = c'x - \rho\xi.$$

If one has a nonlinear characteristic $\varphi(\sigma)$, this notation offers little advantage. Suppose, however, that the characteristic φ is linear, or say that we limit φ to a sufficiently small neighborhood of the origin to make it reasonable to linearize φ, i.e., to replace it by a linear approximation. Let this also be combined with a fundamental system such as (1.1) consisting of a single nth order equation. The resulting system assumes then the form

$$(D^n + \alpha_1 D^{n-1} + \cdots + \alpha_n)\eta = \xi$$

$$D\xi = (\gamma_1 D^{n-1} + \cdots + \gamma_n D)\eta - \rho\xi$$

where the α_h and γ_k are constants. If we set

$$g(D) = D^n + \alpha_1 D^{n-1} + \cdots + \alpha_n$$

$$h(D) = \gamma_1 D^{n-1} + \cdots + \gamma_n D$$

then the system assumes the form

$$g(D)\eta - \xi = 0$$

(2.1)

$$h(D)\eta - (D + \rho)\xi = 0.$$

Now the operators $g(D)$ form what is known in algebra as a *ring of polynomials* and one may apply to such a collection the usual operations of rational algebra: addition, substraction and multiplication (but not division). As a consequence one may solve the system (2.1) in the usual way and obtain the relation

$$\{(D + \rho)g(D) - h(D)\}\eta = 0.$$

The bracket will be denoted by $k(D)$, so that one has to deal with the equation

(2.2) $$k(D)\eta = 0.$$

63

The characteristic equation is

(2.3) $$k(\lambda) = 0.$$

The function $1/k(s)$ is the well-known *transfer function* of the linear theory.

Let m be the degree of $k(\lambda)$ and let the roots $\lambda_1,..., \lambda_m$ of $k(\lambda)$ all be distinct. The general solution of (2.2) is then

$$\eta(t) = C_1 e^{\lambda_1 t} + \cdots + C_m e^{\lambda_m t}.$$

Even if the λ_h are not all distinct n.a.s.c. that $\eta(t)$ and all its derivatives $\to 0$ as $t \to +\infty$ is simply that every $\operatorname{Re} \lambda_h < 0$. This is the full solution of the absolute stability problem in the present instance.

A more complicated situation would correspond to e.g., r parameters $\eta_1,..., \eta_r$ (fundamental parameters) and $r + 1$ equations

$$\sum_k g_{jk}(D)\eta_k - h_j(D)\xi = 0 \qquad (j = 1, 2,..., r + 1).$$

Let

$$\Delta(D) = |g_{jl}(D),..., g_{jr}(D), h_j(D)|.$$

The η's and also ξ are solutions of

$$\Delta(D)\zeta = 0.$$

The characteristic equation is again

(2.4) $$\Delta(\lambda) = 0,$$

and the stability condition: the η's, ξ and all their derivatives $\to 0$ as $t \to +\infty$ is again: the real parts of all the roots of (2.4) must be negative.

§3. Indirect Control

Taking (1.1) as the fundamental (state) system, the indirect control system has naturally the form

(3.1)
$$\eta^{(n)} + \alpha_1 \eta^{(n-1)} + \cdots + \alpha_n \eta = \xi$$
$$\dot{\xi} = \varphi(\sigma)$$
$$\sigma = \gamma_1 \eta^{(n-1)} + \gamma_2 \eta^{(n-2)} + \cdots + \gamma_n \eta - \rho \xi.$$

Such a system may arise under the following conditions. Consider a system S made up of a chain of subsystems $S_1, ..., S_n$ where S_h depends upon the variable η_h and S_h acts upon S_{h+1} in accordance with a relation

$$g_h(D)\eta_h = \eta_{h+1}, \qquad h = 1, 2, ..., n-1$$

except that at the last step there appears the control variable

$$g_n(D)\eta_n = \xi.$$

Here $g_h(D)$ is a polynomial with constant coefficients in the differential parameter D. One may easily realize such a scheme in which for instance the $g_h(D)$ are linear or quadratic. By elimination and setting $\eta_1 = \eta$, one obtains the first equation (3.1):

$$g_1(D)g_2(D) \cdots g_n(D)\eta = \xi.$$

Returning to the system (3.1) observe that here as in (II, §2) and for the same reason it is advantageous to change from the variables η, ξ to new variables ζ, σ so that σ becomes one of the basic variables of the system. This change is defined by $\dot{\eta} = \zeta$ and the new system is

$$\zeta^{(n)} + \alpha_1 \zeta^{(n-1)} + \cdots + \alpha_n \zeta = \varphi(\sigma)$$

(3.2)

$$\dot{\sigma} = \gamma_1 \zeta^{(n-1)} + \cdots + \gamma_n \zeta - \rho\varphi(\sigma).$$

We must prove however the equivalence of the (η, ξ) and (ζ, σ) systems in the sense that the conditions

$$(\eta, \dot{\eta}, ..., \eta^{(n-1)}, \xi) \to 0$$

$$(\zeta, \dot{\zeta}, ..., \zeta^{(n-1)}, \sigma) \to 0$$

are equivalent. For that purpose it is convenient to use the equivalent vector forms e.g. x, ξ and y, σ. They are

$$\dot{x} = Ax - b\xi$$

$$\dot{\xi} = \varphi(\sigma) \qquad \text{where} \qquad c = \begin{pmatrix} \gamma_n \\ \cdot \\ \cdot \\ \cdot \\ \gamma_1 \end{pmatrix}, \qquad b = \begin{pmatrix} 0 \\ 0 \\ \cdot \\ \cdot \\ 0 \\ -1 \end{pmatrix}.$$

$$\sigma = c'x - \rho\xi$$

5. SYSTEMS REPRESENTED BY A SET OF EQUATIONS OF HIGHER ORDER

If we set

$$y_1 = \zeta, \quad y_2 = \dot{\zeta}, ..., y_n = \zeta^{(n-1)}$$

then the transformation that we are considering is given as in (II, §2) by

$$\dot{x} = y = Ax - \xi b$$
$$\sigma = c'x - \rho\xi.$$

The determinant of the transformation is

$$\pm \begin{vmatrix} A & -b \\ \\ c' & -\rho \end{vmatrix} = \gamma_n - \rho\alpha_n$$

and so we require

$$(3.3) \qquad\qquad \gamma_n - \rho\alpha_n \neq 0.$$

This inequality is assumed henceforth. The y, σ system is the standard

$$(3.4) \qquad \dot{y} = Ay - \varphi(\sigma)b$$

$$\dot{\sigma} = c'y - \rho\varphi(\sigma).$$

Hence the (ζ, σ) system is

$$\zeta^{(n)} + \alpha_1\zeta^{(n-1)} + \cdots + \alpha_n\zeta = \varphi(\sigma)$$

$$\dot{\sigma} = \gamma_1\zeta^{(n-1)} + \cdots + \gamma_n\zeta - \rho\varphi(\sigma).$$

The problem of Lurie. It may now be phrased for the system (3.4). Its interpretation for the ζ, σ system is this: to find n.a.s.c. under which if $\zeta(t), \sigma(t)$ is any solution of (3.5) then $\zeta(t), \dot{\zeta}(t), ..., \zeta^{(n-1)}(t), \sigma(t)$ all $\to 0$ as $t \to +\infty$ and this regardless of the choice of an admissible characteristic $\varphi(\sigma)$.

This is a case where the *theory* of the problem is best attacked for the y, σ system (3.4). It is practically a matter of repeating the argument of (II, 2) with the present definitions of A, B, C. Taking then

$$V(y, \sigma) = y'By + \Phi(\sigma)$$

one obtains

$$-\dot{V} = y'Cy + \rho\varphi^2(\sigma) + 2\varphi(\sigma)\,d'y$$

66

where C is arbitrary > 0, B is the unique solution of

$$A'B + BA = -C$$

and the vector d is given explicitly in terms of the actual b, c by

$$-d = \begin{vmatrix} b_{1n} + \frac{1}{2}\gamma_n \\ b_{2n} + \frac{1}{2}\gamma_{n-1} \\ \cdots \\ b_{nn} + \frac{1}{2}\gamma_1 \end{vmatrix}.$$

One may now write the sufficiency condition (F_i) of $(II, 2)$ for absolute stability

$$(F_i) \qquad\qquad \rho > d'C^{-1}d.$$

One will merely recall that (3.4) is a consequence of (F_i) (see III, §4) so that $C > 0$ and (F_i) remain as the only required inequalities.

The remaining considerations regarding an indirect control are the same as before. One must bear in mind, in applying the optimal inequality (III, §2) that the coordinate vector y hence also the vectors b, c are not necessarily the same as the initial vectors y, b, c.

§4. Indirect Control: An Example

We will borrow an example from Letov [1, Chapt. II, §5]—which Letov refers to as the second Bulgakov problem. Using at first the same designation for the constants as Letov, the system is

$$\text{(a)} \quad T^2\ddot{\eta} + U\dot{\eta} + k\eta = T^2\xi$$

$$(4.1) \qquad\qquad \dot{\xi} = \varphi(\sigma)$$

$$\text{(b)} \quad \sigma = a\eta + E\dot{\eta} + G^2\ddot{\eta} - \frac{1}{l}\xi.$$

Here T^2 and G^2 are inertial constants, U and E are dissipative constants and k is a restoring force. At all events U and k are positive.

67

5. SYSTEMS REPRESENTED BY A SET OF EQUATIONS OF HIGHER ORDER

One may change at once the expression of σ, using (4.1a) to

$$\sigma = \left(a - \frac{kG^2}{T^2}\right)\eta + \left(E - \frac{GU}{T^2}\right)\dot{\eta} - \rho\xi,$$

(4.2)

$$\rho = \frac{1}{l} - G^2.$$

We thus see at once that absolute stability will require that $\rho > 0$ and hence that

(4.3)
$$\frac{1}{l} > G^2.$$

We may now change the system to the standard form

$$\ddot{\zeta} + \alpha_1\dot{\zeta} + \alpha_2\zeta = \varphi(\sigma)$$

(4.4)

$$\dot{\sigma} = \gamma_2\zeta + \gamma_1\dot{\zeta} - \rho\varphi(\sigma)$$

with the following values of the constants

$$\alpha_1 = \frac{U}{T^2}, \qquad \alpha_2 = \frac{k}{T^2}$$

(4.5)
$$\gamma_1 = E - \frac{G^2U}{T^2}, \qquad \gamma_2 = a - \frac{kG^2}{T^2}$$

$$\rho = \frac{1}{l} - G^2.$$

The matrix A is

$$A = \begin{pmatrix} 0 & 1 \\ -\alpha_2 & -\alpha_1 \end{pmatrix}$$

and the characteristic equation is

$$s^2 + \alpha_1 s + \alpha_2 = 0.$$

Since α_1, α_2 are positive, the roots have their real parts negative: A is stable. Let the matrices B, C be given by

$$B = \begin{pmatrix} p_0 & q_0 \\ q_0 & r_0 \end{pmatrix}, \qquad C = \begin{pmatrix} p & q \\ q & r \end{pmatrix}.$$

The conditions that $C > 0$ are

(4.6) $$\rho > 0, \qquad pr - q^2 > 0.$$

The relation $A'B + BA = -C$ yields here

$$\begin{pmatrix} -2\alpha_2 q_0, & p_0 - \alpha_1 q_0 - \alpha_2 r_0 \\ p_0 - \alpha_1 q_0 - \alpha_2 r_0, & 2(q_0 - \alpha_1 r_0) \end{pmatrix} = -\begin{pmatrix} p & q \\ q & r \end{pmatrix}$$

or

(4.7) $$\begin{aligned} p &= 2\alpha_2 q_0, \\ q &= \alpha_1 q_0 + \alpha_2 r_0 - p_0 \\ r &= 2(\alpha_1 r_0 - q_0). \end{aligned}$$

We also know from general theory that with A stable, $C > 0$ implies $B > 0$.

Choose as sufficient conditions for stability in the large, the vector relation $d = 0$ (III, 3.2). Here

$$- d = \begin{pmatrix} q_0 + \tfrac{1}{2}\gamma_2 \\ r_0 + \tfrac{1}{2}\gamma_1 \end{pmatrix}.$$

The determinant of the linear system (4.7) in p_0, q_0, r_0 is $4\alpha_1\alpha_2 > 0$. Hence (as we know already) there is a unique solution for p_0, q_0, r_0. We only need q_0 and r_0 and we find

$$q_0 = \frac{p}{2\alpha_2}, \qquad r_0 = \frac{r}{2\alpha_1} + \frac{p}{2\alpha_1\alpha_2}.$$

Therefore

$$- 2d = \begin{pmatrix} \dfrac{p}{\alpha_2} + \gamma_2 \\ \dfrac{r}{\alpha_1} + \dfrac{p}{\alpha_1\alpha_2} + \gamma_1 \end{pmatrix}.$$

Hence $d = 0$ yields the relations

(4.8) $$\begin{aligned} p + \alpha_2\gamma_2 &= 0, \\ p + r\alpha_2 + \alpha_1\alpha_2\gamma_1 &= 0. \end{aligned}$$

69

The first relation already yields $\gamma_2 < 0$. Moreover (4.6) implies $r > 0$ and hence the second of (4.8) yields also $\gamma_1 < 0$. Thus both control constants γ_1, γ_2 must be negative. Upon eliminating p between the two relations of (4.8) there follows $r = \gamma_2 - \alpha_1\gamma_1$. Since $r > 0$ one must have $\gamma_2 > \alpha_1\gamma_1$. Once this is satisfied one takes

$$p = -\alpha_2\gamma_2, \qquad r = \gamma_2 - \alpha_1\gamma_1, \qquad |q| = \sqrt{pr}.$$

Thus, both γ_1, γ_2 negative and $\gamma_2 > \alpha_1\gamma_2$ are sufficient conditions for absolute stability of the system.

In terms of the initial constant, the sufficient conditions are

$$E < \frac{G^2 U}{T^2}, \qquad 0 < \frac{kG^2}{T^2} - a < \frac{U}{T^2}\left(\frac{G^2 U}{T^2} - E\right).$$

§5. Direct Control

The natural equation of a direct control is

$$\eta^{(n)} + \alpha_1\eta^{(n-1)} + \cdots + \alpha_n\eta = \xi$$

(5.1)
$$\xi = \varphi(\sigma)$$

$$\sigma = \gamma_n\eta + \cdots + \gamma_1\eta^{(n-1)}$$

or in the form of a single equation

(5.2)
$$\eta^{(n)} + \alpha_1\eta^{(n-1)} + \cdots + \alpha_n\eta = \varphi(\gamma_n\eta + \cdots + \gamma_1\eta^{(n-1)}).$$

However, if one introduces the auxiliary variables x_h, with $x_1 = \eta$ we obtain the equivalent system

$$\dot{x}_1 = x_2, ..., \dot{x}_{n-1} = x_n$$

(5.3)
$$\dot{x}_n = -\alpha_n x_1 - \alpha_{n-1}x_2 - \cdots - \alpha_1 x_n - \varphi(\sigma)$$

$$\sigma = \gamma_n x_1 + \cdots + \gamma_1 x_n.$$

From this we draw

$$\dot{\sigma} = \gamma_n x_2 + \gamma_{n-1}x_3 + \cdots + \gamma_2 x_n$$

$$-\gamma_1(\alpha_n x_1 + \alpha_{n-1}x_2 + \cdots + \alpha_1 x_n - \varphi(\sigma))$$

or

$$\dot{\sigma} = c'x - \rho\varphi(\sigma)$$

70

where

$$c' = (-\gamma_1\alpha_n, \quad \gamma_{n-1} - \gamma_1\alpha_{n-1}, ..., \gamma_2 - \gamma_1\alpha_1).$$

Also here

$$b' = (0, ..., 0, -1), \qquad \rho = -\gamma_1.$$

Hence

$$d = Bb - \tfrac{1}{2}c = - \begin{vmatrix} b_{1n} - \tfrac{1}{2}\gamma_1\alpha_n \\ b_{2n} + \tfrac{1}{2}(\gamma_n - \gamma_1\alpha_{n-1}) \\ b_{3n} + \tfrac{1}{2}(\gamma_{n-1} - \gamma_1\alpha_{n-2}) \\ \cdot \quad \cdot \quad \cdot \\ b_{nn} + \tfrac{1}{2}(\gamma_2 - \gamma_1\alpha_1) \end{vmatrix}.$$

Here we have once more the difficulty of (IV, §1). It is settled again by reference to LaSalle's theorem (IX, 4.8) leading to the sufficient condition for absolute stability

$$-\gamma_1 = d'C^{-1}d.$$

Chapter 6

DISCONTINUOUS CHARACTERISTICS

Discontinuous characteristics have already been mentioned in the first chapter. (See Fig. 5.) While they clearly escape our general theory, they happen to be of great importance in the applications, and this justifies our discussing them here.

§1. Continuous Approximation of Discontinuous Characteristics

If one takes a strictly practical point of view, one will decide that since in nature instantaneous action is not possible, it is reasonable to replace the two characteristics (a) and (b) of Fig. 5 by those indicated in Fig. 6. For the type (a) the approximation behaves in accordance with (I, §1). However, for the type (b) property II of (I, §1): $\sigma\varphi(\sigma) > 0$ for $\sigma \neq 0$, is violated and so further considerations are required. We discuss separately indirect and direct controls.

Indirect control. Let the system be (II, 2.3), referred to the coordinates y, σ. In endeavoring to apply our general method, we meet with the difficulty that $V(y, \sigma)$, formed as before, is not positive definite since it vanishes for $y = 0$, $\alpha < \sigma < \beta$. The best way to deal with this difficulty is by a generalization of Liapunov's theory due to Zubov. All that is

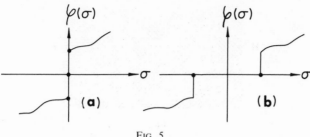

FIG. 5

required is the generalization of asymptotic stability. Now in Zubov's book [1, p. 48], the appropriate result is found. Essentially Zubov shows that in the Liapunov treatment one may replace the isolated critical point (the origin) *by any closed invariant set M*. We recall that such a set (open or closed) is just a collection of complete paths. That is, if p is any point of M, then the complete path (forward and backward) of p lies in M. In our case the segment $\alpha \leq \sigma \leq \beta$, $y = 0$, is an invariant set, since each point is a critical point of the system. Thus one may apply directly the Liapunov results on asymptotic stability. In short, all our developments for an indirect control are valid save that absolute stability is to be interpreted in the "practical sense" that all solutions $(y(t), \sigma(t))$ tend to $(0, p)$ where p is some point of the (open) interval α, β of Fig. 6b. This is as far as one may go.

Direct control. Take the equation (IV, 1.1) for the system. This time one verifies at once that the function $V(x)$ of (IV, §1) is still positive definite and so there is no difficulty in connection with this function.

§2. Direct Discussion of Discontinuities

We shall now attack directly the problem of discontinuities.
One might be inclined to the facile view that it suffices to take the

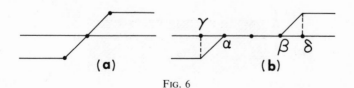

FIG. 6

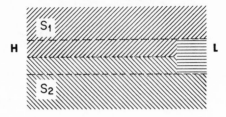

FIG. 7

situation just considered and "pass to the limit." Unfortunately this does not happen to be the case.

As a preliminary step it is necessary to say something about discontinuities in differential equations in general. In this we follow in substance André and Seibert [1].

Let H be a hyperplane ($(n - 1)$ subspace) of the n space of x. One may select the coordinate system so that H is the subspace $x_1 = 0$. What we propose to do is to define an n vector system

(2.1) $$\dot{x} = X(x)$$

discontinuous across H. Consider a narrow layer L (region) of our space, with center H, defined by $|x_1| < \delta, \delta > 0$ and small (Fig. 7). Let $S_i, i = 1, 2$ be the two regions of n space separated by H, that is the regions S_1: $x_1 > 0$ and S_2: $x_1 < 0$ and let $R_i, i = 1, 2$, be the region consisting of S_i plus L. Thus R_1 is the region $x_1 > -\delta$, and R_2 the region $x_1 < \delta$ (Fig. 8).

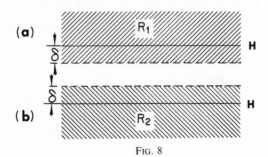

FIG. 8

74

§2. DIRECT DISCUSSION OF DISCONTINUITIES

Consider now two distinct n vector systems

(2.2) $$\dot{x} = X^i(x), \qquad i = 1, 2$$

where X^i is of class C^1 in R_i. Define X as coinciding with X^i in the set $\bar{S}_i = S_i$ plus H. The resulting system (2.1) will (generally) have the hyperplane H as discontinuity.

The procedure just followed offers the great advantage that the solutions of (2.1) in R_i are naturally extended up to all points of H without requiring any "limit" complications which are really foreign to the main theme. Furthermore, it is well known that continuity over a closed set such as $\bar{S}_i$ must actually be defined over a slightly larger open set, here the region R_i.

It is pertinent to observe that our mode of definition does correspond to that occurring in the applications where an inevitable amount of inertia will carry a path reaching the hyperplane H slightly beyond H.

We will assume that neither of the systems (2.2) has a critical point on H, that is that $X^i(x) \neq 0, i = 1, 2$ on the hyperplane.

Regarding any path γ of (2.1) what is of interest is its behavior on $\bar{S}_i = S_i$ plus H, and not actually throughout R_i. Concerning γ in S_i we restrict ourselves to the following possibilities as to its approach to a point x_0 of H:

(a) $\gamma \to x_0$ with increasing t and as t tends to a certain value t_0, and without tangency to H at x_0. In standard terminology $x_0 = x(t_0 -)$.

(b) The same but $x_0 = x(t_0 +)$ (γ tends to x_0 with decreasing t).

(c) $\gamma \to x_0$ and is tangent to H at x_0 in $\bar{S}_i$.

(d) Finally, of practical importance is the case when one of the two systems has a path through x_0 running in the hyperplane H itself.

While the cases just described cover all the situations envisaged below, our general scheme may readily take care of more complicated

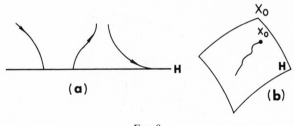

$$\text{(a)} \qquad \text{(b)}$$

FIG. 9

75

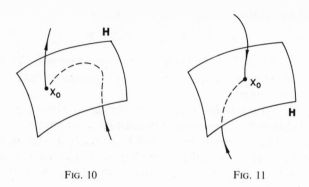

FIG. 10   FIG. 11

situations. Notice at all events that one may well replace the hyperplane *H* by a manifold *M* of some sort.

One refers to the hyperplane *H* or manifold *M* as *switching* hyperplane or manifold for the system (1.1).

Still confining the discussion to *H* upon combining what happens on both sides of *H* one will find for x_0 the following possibilities:

(1) Of the two arcs tending to x_0 on S_1 and S_2 the one, say in $S_1 \to x_0$, and the other in S_2 leaves x_0 (Fig. 10). We consider then the path and solution in S_2 as the extension of the solution in S_1 beyond x_0. A point such as x_0 is known as a *transition point.*

(2) The arcs on both sides of x_0 tend to the point x_0 (Fig. 11). We have then an *end point.* The solution from either side cannot be extended beyond x_0.

(3) The arcs on both sides leave the point x_0 (Fig. 12). We have then a *starting point.* Here again there is no possible extension across the point x_0.

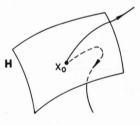

FIG. 12

76

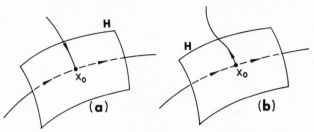

FIG. 13

(4) On one side an arc is tangent to the switching hyperplane as indicated in Fig. 13 or else rests upon the hyperplane at both ends as in Fig. 14. In both cases we will refer to the point as *mixed*.

(5) The system $(2.1)_1$ gives rise to an arc γ_1 in S_1 tending to x_0 and the system $(2.1)_2$ has an arc γ_2 in H leaving x_0 (Fig. 15), or else γ_i tends to x_0 in H and γ_2 leaves x_0 in S_1 (arrows of Fig. 15 reversed). As a variant, not required later, both γ_1, γ_2 tend to or both leave x_0. These situations really correspond to the cases $1, 2, 3$ with one of the arcs ending at x_0 situated in the hyperplane H.

(6) Still another highly interesting situation, as yet but little considered for dimensions above two will only be described in the plane. It corresponds to several switching arcs issued from the same point, say the origin. Let there be s switching arcs $\Gamma_1,...,\Gamma_s$ and let U_h be the sector bounded by Γ_h and Γ_{h+1}, $(\Gamma_{s+1} = \Gamma_1)$. There are defined s systems

$$(2.3) \qquad \dot{x}_i = X_i^h(x_1, x_2), \qquad h = 1, 2,..., s$$

where for the system $(2.3)_h$ the functions X_i^h, X_2^h are of class C^1 in an

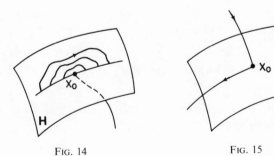

FIG. 14   FIG. 15

77

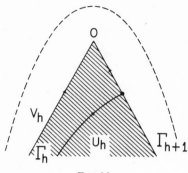

FIG. 16

open region V_h which contain the sector U_h together with Γ_h and Γ_{h+1}, and has no critical point in V_h. Moreover Γ_h is a path of $(2.3)_h$ tending to the origin with increasing t. A path γ of $(2.3)_h$ will run, e.g., for increasing t till it meets Γ_{h+1} at a point x_0, and will continue beyond x_0 with the arc of Γ_{h+1} from x_0 to the origin. The effect of this situation is to make the origin reached by all paths in finite time (Fig. 16).

The differential equation

$$\dot{x}_i = X_i(x_1, x_2), \qquad i = 1, 2$$

for this situation is defined by $X_i = X_i^h$ on U_h plus Γ_h and it is (generally) discontinuous along the switching arcs Γ_h.

Returning to the simpler cases $1, 2, 3$, one may localize in H the different types of points as follows. At the point x_0 of H the arc γ in R_i will tend to or away from x_0 accordingly as $X_1^i(0, x_2^0, ..., x_n^0) < 0$ or > 0. Hence, excluding the points where this quantity vanishes we will have:

transition point $\left.\begin{array}{c} \\ \\ \end{array}\right\}$ wherever the product

starting or end point

$$X^1(0, x_2, ..., x_n) X^2(0, x_2, ..., x_n) \begin{cases} > 0 \\ \quad . \\ < 0 \end{cases}$$

The inequalities characterize then the two types of sets in H: transition sets and starting or end point sets.

§3. Some Examples

The examples of discontinuity to be discussed, of systems of dimension one and two, mostly with discontinuities of the type of Fig. 5, will serve to obtain some insight into the complications that may arise. In all the examples one may take as sets R_i the whole plane itself, so that no further mention of these sets will be required.

As our first example, take the indirect control system of (I, §3): represented by the system (I, 3.5) or

$$\dot{y} = -ky + \varphi(\sigma)$$

(3.1)

$$\dot{\sigma} = cy - \rho\varphi(\sigma),$$

where now all letters denote scalars. As for φ we take the type of Fig. 5a, explicitly

$$\varphi(\sigma) = \begin{cases} M, & \sigma > 0 \\ -M, & \sigma < 0. \end{cases}$$

We also assume $k > 0$.

In the present instance one may integrate. As above, let S_1 represent the half plane $\sigma > 0$ and S_2 the half plane $\sigma < 0$. The system for S_1 is

(3.2) $$\dot{y} = -ky + M, \qquad \dot{\sigma} = cy - \rho M.$$

The solutions may actually be defined for S_1 plus the line $\sigma = 0$ (the y axis). We may write

$$\frac{d}{dt}\left(y - \frac{M}{k}\right) = -k\left(y - \frac{M}{k}\right),$$

which integrates as

$$y = \alpha e^{-kt} + \frac{M}{k}.$$

This yields

$$\dot{\sigma} = c\left(\alpha e^{-kt} + \frac{M}{k}\right) - \rho M$$

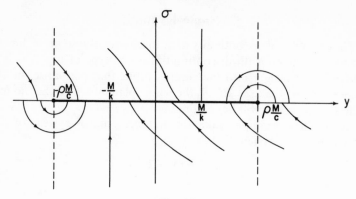

FIG. 17

which integrates as

$$\sigma = -\frac{c\alpha}{k}e^{-kt} + M\left(\frac{c}{k} - \rho\right)t + \beta.$$

The solution reaches $\sigma = 0$ for $t = 0$ if $\beta = c\alpha/k$. Thus

$$\sigma = \frac{c\alpha}{k}(1 - e^{-kt}) + M\left(\frac{c}{k} - \rho\right)t$$

which must be taken only in the half plane $\sigma \geqq 0$.

In the lower half plane the system is

$$\dot{y} = -ky - M, \qquad \dot{\sigma} = cy + \rho M$$

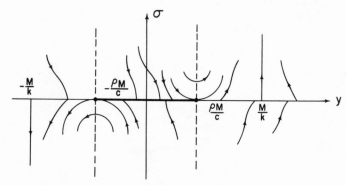

FIG. 18

with solutions

$$y = \gamma e^{-kt} - \frac{M}{k}$$

$$\sigma = \frac{c\gamma}{k}(1 - e^{-kt}) - M\left(\frac{c}{k} - \rho\right)t.$$

We are interested in the behavior of the paths on both sides, but near to the y axis. Here several cases must be distinguished according to the values of certain constants.

I. $\rho k > c > 0$. The general situation is described by Fig. 17. The points of the arc $|y| < \rho(M/c)$ of the y axis are end points and the ends of this arc, the points $y = \pm\rho(M/c)$, are transition points.

II. $c > \rho k > 0$. The general description is indicated in Fig. 18. The same arc as before consists of end points.

III. $c < 0$. Set $c = -c_0$. Then if $c_0 < \rho k$ the situation is the symmetric of Fig. 18 with respect to the y axis while if $c_0 > \rho k$, it is the symmetric of Fig. 17 relative to the same axis.

An entirely analogous treatment may be applied to the more complicated characteristic of Fig. 5b. Let the system be (3.1) with

$$\varphi(\sigma) = \begin{cases} M, & \sigma > \alpha > 0 \\ 0, & -\alpha < \sigma < +\alpha \\ -M, & \sigma < -\alpha. \end{cases}$$

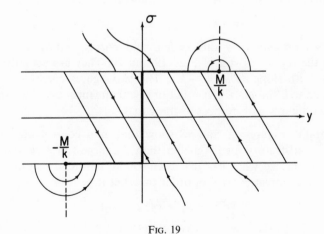

FIG. 19

81

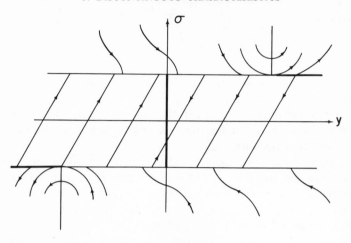

FIG. 20

This time we have

$$\dot{y} = \begin{cases} -ky + M, & \dot{\sigma} = cy - \rho M, & \sigma > \alpha \\ \\ -ky - M, & \dot{\sigma} = cy + \rho M, & \sigma < -\alpha. \end{cases}$$

Hence, the upper halves of our graphs will be valid for $\sigma > \alpha$ and their lower halves for $\sigma < -\alpha$. In between the common system is

$$\dot{y} = -ky, \qquad \dot{\sigma} = cy, \qquad |\sigma| \leqq \alpha.$$

The arcs represented by this system and corresponding to $c > 0$ are those in the region $|\sigma| < \alpha$ of Figs. 19 and 20. They are actually parallel segments with slope $d\sigma/dy = -k/c$. The two figures correspond respectively to $\rho c < k$ and $\rho c > k, c > 0$. For $c < 0$ one must take the symmetric of the two figures with respect to the y axis.

REMARK. Figures 17 and 18 show that as a control operation the scheme is satisfactory for $|y|$ greater than the largest of M/k and $\rho(M/c)$.

To emphasize what has just been found, consider an example of a discontinuous direct control of order two. Let it be

$$\dot{x}_1 = -x_1 + \varphi(x_1 + x_2)$$
$$\dot{x}_2 = -3x_2 + \varphi(x_1 + x_2)$$

82

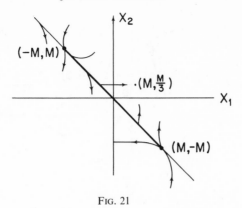

FIG. 21

with

$$\varphi(x_1 + x_2) = \begin{cases} M \\ -M \end{cases} \quad \text{for} \quad \begin{cases} x_1 + x_2 > 0 \\ x_1 + x_2 < 0. \end{cases}$$

Here the switching line is $x_1 + x_2 = 0$. Consider first the system above the line. We have

$$\dot{x}_1 = -(x_1 - M), \qquad \dot{x}_2 = -3\left(x_2 - \frac{M}{3}\right).$$

Tangency to the line will occur where

$$\frac{-3(x_2 - M/3)}{-(x_1 - M)} = -1, \qquad x_1 + x_2 = 0$$

or $-x_1 = x_2 = M$. The behavior is shown in Fig. 21 above the line. The behavior below the switching line is just the symmetric with respect to the origin of the one just obtained. Between the points $(-M, M)$ and $(M, -M)$ all points are starting points. Outside they are transition points. The ends of the segment are mixed points.

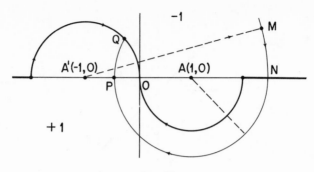

FIG. 22

§4. Special Switching Lines

It is evident that taking the locus $\sigma = 0$ as switching line has resulted in making the origin virtually inaccessible from nearby points. This could not be more opposed to the very purpose of a control.

For some systems with discontinuous control one may construct switching lines so as to restore the stability of the origin. We borrow the example from Bushaw [1, p. 36]. Let the system be

(4.1)

(a) $\dot{x} = y, \qquad \dot{y} = -x + M$

(b) $\dot{x} = y, \qquad \dot{y} = -x - M.$

The two systems can be written respectively

$$(x \overset{.}{+} M)y = y, \qquad \dot{y} = -(x - M)$$

$$(x \overset{.}{+} M)y = y, \qquad \dot{y} = -(x + M)$$

whose paths are the circles of center $(0, \pm M)$. Both are described clockwise. The switching line is the heavy line of Fig. 22.

The system (4.1a) prevails below the switching line and (4.1b) prevails above it. The immediate effect of the switching line is to make all paths tend to the origin *in finite time*. A typical path is $MNPQO$ of Fig. 22, with the end arc QO part of the switching line.

§5. Multiple Feedback Switching Line

The switching lines or spaces are equally interesting in the case of multiple feedbacks. We will merely illustrate this by an example more or less inspired by LaSalle [3]. The system is in two variables.

(5.1)
$$\dot{x}_1 = -x_1 + \tfrac{3}{2}u_1 + \tfrac{1}{2}u_2$$

$$\dot{x}_2 = -2x_2 + 2u_1 + 4u_2$$

The u_j play the same role as the f_j in (IV, 10), and just take the values ± 1. Consider first $u_1 = u_2 = 1$. The system is then

(5.2)
$$\dot{x}_1 = -x_1 + 2, \qquad \dot{x}_2 = -2x_2 + 6$$

which may also be written

$$(x_1 - 2)\dot{} = -(x_1 - 2), \qquad (x_2 - 3)\dot{} = -2(x_2 - 3).$$

Hence the paths in the plane are those of

(5.3)
$$\dot{x}_1 = -x_1, \qquad \dot{x}_2 = -2x_2$$

shifted by $(2, 3)$. The paths of (4.3) are given by $x_1 = \alpha e^{-t}$, $x_2 = \beta e^{-\beta t}$ or $x_1^2 = \gamma x_2$, that is they are vertical parabolas. We take as one of the switching arcs (Fig. 23) the arc AO of the shifted parabola (vertex $(2, 3)$) through the origin. For $u_1 = -1$, $u_2 = 1$ the system is

$$(x_1 + 1)\dot{} = -(x_1 + 1), \qquad (x_2 - 1)\dot{} = -2(x_2 - 1)$$

with parabolas of vertex $(-1, 1)$ and we take as switching arc the arc OB of the parabola through the origin. The other two switching arcs

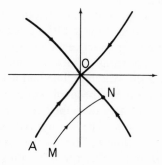

FIG. 23

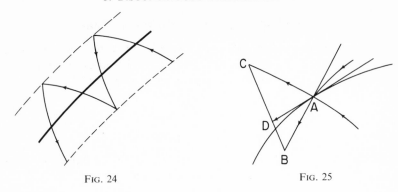

FIG. 24   FIG. 25

correspond to $u_1 = -1$, $u_2 = -1$ and $u_1 = 1$, $u_2 = -1$. They are the symmetrical OA', OB' of the arcs OA, OB. The regions of operation of the systems corresponding to the four sets of values of u_1, u_2 are marked on the figure as $(1, 1)$,..., the path issued from a point M is MNO and it is clear that here again the origin is reached from every point of the plane in finite time.

§6. Complementary Remarks

It is evident that the switching line scheme may be greatly expanded but we shall not attempt this here. What has been done suffices to show that the strict treatment of the discontinuous case brings in altogether new elements, for instance an entire segment of end points. Their presence contradicts entirely the notion that in spite of the discontinuity the origin remains a "nice" critical point.

It is interesting to point out that various authors have endeavored to define a natural extension of the solutions about an end point beyond or along the switching line. In practice, one is apt to observe along an end point segment what is known as "chatter," which occurs when the solutions get a little beyond the switching line and act as indicated in Fig. 24.

Still another extension has been proposed recently by Filipov [1]. The application here is clearly described in Fig. 25 for the case $n = 1$ and a smooth switching curve. The vectors AB, AC are the velocities on both sides of the switching line L. The segment AB intersects the tangent to L at A at a point D and the vector AD represents the velocity vector in L for the extended motion.

86

Chapter 7

SOME RECENT RESULTS OF
V. M. POPOV

Recently the Romanian applied mathematician, V. M. Popov, inspired perhaps by the classical Laplace transform methods of linear analysis, utilized with telling effect Fourier transforms in an attack on control problems (Popov [2]). This provided the impulsion for Yacubovich and then Kalman to return to more algebraic methods with noteworthy new results. In particular Kalman succeeded in completing Popov's work in an important way.

We shall deal partly with the work of Yacubovich and Kalman in the next chapter. The present chapter is devoted to a presentation of Popov's very original first results.

§1. Generalities. The Theorems of Popov

In his work Popov considers a system in the following form, slightly different from our standard form (II, §2):

$$
\begin{aligned}
\text{(a)} \quad & \dot{x} = Ax - \varphi(\sigma)b \\
\text{(b)} \quad & \dot{\xi} = \varphi(\sigma) \\
\text{(c)} \quad & \sigma = c'x - \gamma\xi.
\end{aligned}
$$

(1.1)

In this system all the letters have the same meaning as in (II, §2). In particular the matrix A is still stable. The scalar γ is new.

Existence and uniqueness of solutions are dealt with as they are at the end of the Introduction.

The general purpose is still to find conditions for absolute stability (Lurie).

A necessary condition for absolute stability is that $x = 0$, $\sigma = 0$ be the only critical point, i.e., the only solution of

$$Ax - b\varphi(\sigma) = 0, \qquad \varphi(\sigma) = 0.$$

Since $\varphi(\sigma) = 0$ when and only when $\sigma = 0$, and since A^{-1} exists this condition is actually fulfilled.

Observe that if $\gamma = 0$ then the system (1.1) is, for control purposes, the system

$$\dot{x} = Ax - b\varphi(c'x),$$

that is, it is a *direct control*. As we wish to discuss first indirect controls we assume for the present that $\gamma \neq 0$. As a matter of fact:

(1.2) *Under the assumption that $\gamma \neq 0$, a necessary condition for absolute stability is $\gamma > 0$.*

Absolute stability requires that the system (1.1) be asymptotically stable for $\varphi(\sigma) = \mu\sigma$, $\mu > 0$. That is, the system

$$\dot{x} = (A - \mu bc')x + \mu b\gamma\xi$$

$$\dot{\xi} = \mu c'x - \mu\gamma\xi$$

must be asymptotically stable for $\mu > 0$. A paraphrase of the argument of (IV, §5) [case (a)] yields here simply that one must have $\gamma > 0$.

Since $\gamma \neq 0$ the transformation $(x, \xi) \to (x, \sigma)$ defined by $x = x$, $\sigma = c'x - \gamma\xi$ is nonsingular. It transforms the system (1.1) into the equivalent system

(1.3)
$$\text{(a)} \quad \dot{x} = Ax - \varphi(\sigma)b$$
$$\text{(b)} \quad \dot{\sigma} = c'Ax - \rho\varphi(\sigma)$$
$$\text{(c)} \quad \rho = \gamma + c'b$$

which represents a standard indirect control such as (II, 2.3), and this *without changing the system variable x*. Thus (1.1) represents essentially a standard indirect control.

88

Conversely there is a nonsingular transformation of coordinates reducing the standard indirect control system of (II, 2.1) *to the Popov type* (1.1). *Hence Popov's system represents a completely general indirect control.*
Write the fundamental system (II, 2.1) as follows:

$$\dot{x} = Ax - b_0\xi$$
$$\dot{\xi} = \varphi(\sigma)$$
$$\sigma = c'x - \rho\xi.$$

Introduce the auxiliary variable

$$z = x - A^{-1}b_0\xi.$$

The transformation $(x, \xi) \to (z, \xi)$ is manifestly nonsingular. Hence for all stability purposes the auxiliary (z, ξ) system will be fully equivalent to the fundamental system. The (z, ξ) system is immediately found to be

$$\dot{z} = Az - A^{-1}b_0\varphi(\sigma)$$
$$\dot{\xi} = \varphi(\sigma)$$
$$\sigma = c'z - (\rho - c'A^{-1}b_0)\xi.$$

This is a Popov system with

$$b = -A^{-1}b_0, \qquad \gamma = \rho - c'A^{-1}b_0.$$

From this Popov system one may pass to the fundamental system (1.1) by the relations

$$b_0 = -Ab, \qquad \rho = \gamma + c'b.$$

REMARK. In the designations of (II, §2) we have shown (LaSalle) (III, §2) that $\rho > c'A^{-1}b$. Since the previous c' is the present $c'A^{-1}b$ the same relation reads now $\gamma = \rho - c'b > 0$. Thus one of the present conditions for absolute stability is the same as LaSalle's condition.

Certain noteworthy expressions and their Fourier transforms must now be introduced. As in (IV, §4) set $A_z = zE - A$ so that $|A_z| = 0$ is the characteristic equation of A. Since A has no pure complex characteristic roots $|A_{i\omega}| \neq 0$ for all real ω, hence $A_{i\omega}^{-1}$ is defined for all such ω.

Recall that $X(t) = \exp(At)$ is the canonical solution of the matrix differential equation $\dot{X} = AX$, that is, the solution such that $X(0) = E$.

An important function occurring in the proof of Popov's first theorem is defined by

$$v(t) = c'e^{At}b.$$

89

By definition the Fourier transform of a function $u(t)$ is the integral (if it exists)

(1.4)
$$\mathscr{F}(u) = \int_0^{+\infty} e^{-i\omega t} u(t)\, dt$$

and similarly for vectors and matrices. In particular

$$\mathscr{F}(v) = N(i\omega) = c' \int_0^{+\infty} \exp(-A_{i\omega} \cdot t)\, dt \cdot b$$

$$-c' \cdot A_{i\omega}^{-1} [\exp(-A_{i\omega}t)]_0^{+\infty} b = c' A_{i\omega}^{-1} b.$$

As this last expression will be of constant occurrence in the sequel we may note at once the general property:

(1.5) *The expressions $c' A_z^{-1} b$, $c' A_{i\omega}^{-1} b$ are invariant with respect to transformations of coordinates.*

In fact from (1.1) the transformation of coordinates $x \to Px$ yields

$$b \to P^{-1}b, \qquad c' \to c'P, \qquad A_z \to P^{-1}A_z P, \qquad A_z^{-1} \to P^{-1}A_z^{-1}P.$$

From this follows as asserted that $c' A_z^{-1} b$ remains unchanged.

In addition to $N(i\omega)$ there will be required the function

$$G(i\omega) = N(i\omega) + \frac{\gamma}{i\omega} = c' A_{i\omega}^{-1} b + \frac{\gamma}{i\omega}.$$

(In §7 the function $G(z)$ will be shown to be a "transfer" function).

We may now state the two theorems of Popov:

(1.6) **First theorem of Popov.** *A sufficient condition for the absolute stability of the system* (1.1) *is that for some nonnegative number q and all real ω we have*

(1.7)
$$\mathrm{Re}\{(1 + i\omega q)G(i\omega)\} = \mathrm{Re}\{(1 + i\omega q)(c' A_{i\omega}^{-1} b)\} + q\gamma \geqq 0.$$

The importance of this result is enhanced by

(1.8) **Popov's second theorem.** *If the absolute stability of the system* (1.1) *may be determined by means of a Liapunov function $V(x, \sigma)$ of the form "quadratic in x, σ plus $\beta \int_0^\sigma \varphi(\sigma)\, d\sigma$" then there exists a $q \geqq 0$ such that* (1.7) *holds.*

To sum up, the first theorem asserts that the inequality (1.7) is a sufficient condition for absolute stability, while the second implies, in

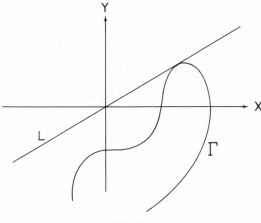

FIG. 26

particular, that if our inequality (F_i) holds then (1.7) holds also. Thus (1.7) is broader. This is assuredly striking enough.

The inequality (1.7) may be given, with Popov an interesting geometric interpretation. Set

$$c'A_{i\omega}^{-1}b + \frac{\gamma}{i\omega} = S_1(\omega) + i\omega S_2(\omega)$$

where S_1, S_2 are real rational functions of ω, in fact continuous for all ω. Then (1.7) yields

$$S_1(\omega) - q\omega S_2(\omega) \geqq 0.$$

In the real x, y plane, consider the line

$$L: \quad x - qy = 0.$$

According to (1.7) the curve $\Gamma: x = S_1(\omega)$, $y = \omega S_2(\omega)$ has a tangent from the origin in quadrants 1 and 3 (Fig. 26) and is otherwise located below this tangent. The curve Γ is of the type called *unicursal* in algebraic geometry.

§2. Preliminary Properties

Before taking up the proofs of Popov's theorems it is convenient to discuss certain preliminary properties. Incidentally we will write systematically $\varphi(t)$, $\Phi(t)$ for $\varphi(\sigma(t))$, $\Phi(\sigma(t))$.

91

I. From (1.1a) there follows the basic condition (Lefschetz [1, p. 72]):

(2.1) $$x(t) = X(t)x_0 - \int_0^t X(t - \tau)b\varphi(\tau)\, d\tau,$$

where $x_0 = x(0)$, and similarly later $\sigma_0 = \sigma(0)$, etc.

From (2.1) and (1.1c) there follows

(2.2) $$\sigma(t) = c'(X(t)x_0 - \int_0^t X(t - \tau)b\varphi(\tau)\, d\tau) - \gamma\xi(t)$$

$$= c'X(t)x_0 - \int_0^t v(t - \tau)\varphi(\tau)\, d\tau - \gamma\xi(t).$$

II. Let $g(t)$ be a polynomial and let m be a positive constant. Let also

$$h(t) = g(t)\, e^{-mt}.$$

Since

$$|g(t)|\, e^{-(m-k)t}, \qquad 0 < k < m$$

is bounded for $t \geqq 0$ there is a positive constant C such that

(2.3) $$|h(t)| < Ce^{-kt} \qquad \text{for} \quad t \geqq 0.$$

Let $h(t)$ be a finite sum of expressions $g(t)e^{\lambda t}$, $\operatorname{Re} \lambda < 0$. If $0 < k <$ least $-\operatorname{Re} \lambda$ then (2.3) holds also. We refer to $h(t)$ as *quasi exponential*. In particular since the matrix A is stable both $v(t)$ and $\dot{v}(t)$ are quasi exponential and so satisfy relations such as (2.3). We may in fact choose fixed C, k such that

(2.4) $$|v(t)|, \quad |\dot{v}(t)| < Ce^{-kt}, \qquad t \geqq 0.$$

III. If $k > 0$ and $f(t) \to 0$ as $t \to \infty$ then likewise

$$g(t) = \int_0^t e^{-k(t-\tau)} f(\tau)\, d\tau \to 0 \qquad \text{as} \quad t \to +\infty$$

For

$$|g(t)| \leqq e^{-kt} \int_0^t e^{k\tau} |f(\tau)|\, d\tau = h(t),$$

and by the rule of l'Hospital as $t \to +\infty$:

$$\lim h(t) = \lim |f(t)| = 0.$$

IV. By *convolution* of two functions $f(t)$, $g(t)$ is meant the operation $*$ defined by

$$f * g = \int_0^t f(\tau) g(t - \tau) \, d\tau$$

and we note that $f * g = g * f$. With this notation one may write (2.1) and (2.2) as

$$x = X(t)x_0 - X(t) * b\varphi(t)$$
$$\sigma = c'X(t)x_0 - v(t) * \varphi(t) - \gamma\xi(t).$$

The basic properties are

(2.5)
$$\mathscr{F}(f_1 * f_2) = \mathscr{F}(f_1)\mathscr{F}(f_2)$$

$$\int_{-\infty}^{+\infty} f(t)\bar{g}(t) \, dt = \int_{-\infty}^{+\infty} \mathscr{F}(f)\bar{\mathscr{F}}(g) \, d\omega,$$

and if g is real

(2.6)
$$\int_{-\infty}^{+\infty} f(t)g(t) \, dt = \int_{-\infty}^{+\infty} \mathscr{F}(f)\bar{\mathscr{F}}(g) \, d\omega.$$

(For these properties consult Doetsch [1, pp. 157–163] and Titchmarsh [1, p. 50].)

Of course one must assume that the integrals just written do exist.

§3. Proof of Popov's First Theorem

Introduce the following functions

$$\varphi_T(t) = \begin{cases} \varphi(t) & \text{for} \quad 0 \le t \le T \\ 0 & \text{otherwise,} \end{cases}$$

$$\mu(t) = -(v(t) + q\dot{v}(t));$$

$$\lambda(t) = \int_0^t \mu(t - \tau)\varphi_T(\tau) \, d\tau - q\rho\varphi_T(t) = \mu(t) * \varphi_T(t) - q\rho\varphi_T(t);$$

$$\zeta(t) = c'(X(t) + q\dot{X}(t))x_0.$$

Now (2.2) yields

$$\dot{\sigma}(t) = c'\dot{X}(t)x_0 - \frac{d}{dt}\int_0^t v(t - \tau)\varphi(\tau)\,d\tau - \gamma\varphi(t)$$

$$= c'\dot{X}(t)x_0 - \int_0^t \dot{v}(t - \tau)\varphi(\tau)\,d\tau - \rho\varphi(t).$$

From this and (2.2) follows

(3.1) $$\lambda(t) = \sigma(t) + q\dot{\sigma}(t) + \gamma\xi(t) - \zeta(t), \quad 0 \leqq t \leqq T.$$

Another required property of $\lambda(t)$ is:

(3.2) *There exist positive constants k, C such that for $t \geqq T$:*

(3.2a) $$|\lambda(t)| < Ce^{-kt}.$$

Since both $v(t)$ and $\dot{v}(t)$ are quasi exponential so is $\mu(t)$. Hence for $t \geqq T$ and some $k, C > 0$

$$|\lambda(t)| < C\int_0^t e^{-k(t-\tau)}|\varphi_T(\tau)|\,d\tau = Ce^{-kt}\int_0^T e^{k\tau}|\varphi_T(\tau)|\,d\tau$$

which is (3.2a) with suitable C.

Taking into account (3.2) or the quasi exponential property or continuity of the various functions integrated in the sequel, all our integrals will be meaningful—a property not emphasized later.

Set now

$$L(i\omega) = \mathscr{F}(\lambda), \qquad F(i\omega) = \mathscr{F}(\varphi_T).$$

By a basic property of Fourier integrals

$$\mathscr{F}(\dot{v}) = \int_0^{+\infty} e^{-i\omega t}\dot{v}(t)\,dt = i\omega N(i\omega) - c'b$$

$$= i\omega N(i\omega) + \gamma - \rho,$$

$$\mathscr{F}(\lambda) = L(i\omega) = -\{N(i\omega)(1 + i\omega q) + q\gamma\}F(i\omega).$$

Define now the functions

$$\theta(T) = \int_0^{+\infty} \lambda(t)\varphi_T(t)\,dt.$$

§3. PROOF OF POPOV'S FIRST THEOREM

(3.3) *The inequality* (1.7) *(hypothesis of Theorem 1.6) implies that* $\theta(T) \leq 0$.

In fact referring to (2.6)

$$\theta(T) = \int_{-\infty}^{+\infty} L(i\omega)\overline{F(i\omega)}\, d\omega$$

$$= -\int_{-\infty}^{+\infty} \{N(i\omega)(1 + i\omega q) + q\gamma\}F(i\omega)\overline{F(i\omega)}\, d\omega$$

$$= -\int_{-\infty}^{+\infty} |F(i\omega)|^2(N(i\omega)(1 + i\omega q) + q\gamma)\, d\omega$$

$$= \frac{-1}{2\pi}\int_{-\infty}^{+\infty} |F(i\omega)|^2\{\operatorname{Re} N(i\omega)(1 + i\omega q) + q\gamma\}\, d\omega$$

$$= \frac{-1}{2\pi}\int_{-\infty}^{+\infty} |F(i\omega)|^2 \operatorname{Re}(1 + i\omega q)G(i\omega)\, d\omega$$

As a consequence of (1.7) the last integral is ≥ 0 and so (3.3) follows. Upon combining (3.1) and (3.3) there follows the important inequality

$$(3.4) \quad \int_0^T \sigma(t)\varphi(t)\, dt + q\int_0^T \dot{\sigma}(t)\varphi(t)\, dt + \gamma\int_0^T \xi(t)\varphi(t)\, dt \leq \int_0^T \zeta(t)\varphi(t)\, dt.$$

One must analyze now all these integrals.

The left-hand side of (3.4):

Since $\sigma\varphi(\sigma) > 0$ for all $\sigma \neq 0$, for all T:

$$(3.5) \qquad \int_0^T \sigma(t)\varphi(t)\, dt > 0.$$

Regarding the second integral

$$(3.6) \qquad \int_0^T \dot{\sigma}(t)\varphi(t)\, dt = \Phi(T) - \Phi(0).$$

Finally the third integral yields

$$(3.7) \qquad \int_0^T \xi(t)\varphi(t)\, dt = \int_0^T \xi(t)\dot{\xi}(t)\, dt = \frac{\xi^2(T) - {\xi_0}^2}{2}.$$

7. SOME RECENT RESULTS OF V. M. POPOV

At the right-hand side of (3.4):

$$\int_0^T \zeta(t)\varphi(t)\, dt = \int_0^T \zeta(t)\dot{\xi}(t)\, dt$$

$$= [\zeta(t)\xi(t)]_0^T - \int_0^T \xi(t)\dot{\zeta}(t)\, dt.$$

Let $\xi_1 = \sup|\xi(t)|$ in $0 \leq t \leq T$. Since ζ is quasi exponential, and proportional to $\|x_0\|$, if $u = \|x_0\| + \xi_0$, then

$$\left|[\zeta(t)\xi(t)]_0^T\right| < C_1 u\xi_1, \qquad C_1 > 0.$$

Since $\dot{\zeta}(t)$ is quasi exponential of the same nature as $\zeta(t)$

$$\left|\int_0^T \xi(t)\dot{\zeta}(t)\, dt\right| < C_2 u\xi_1, \qquad C_2 > 0.$$

Hence with $C > 0$ and independent of T:

(3.8)
$$\left|\int_0^T \zeta(t)\varphi(t)\, dt\right| < Cu\xi_1.$$

Upon combining the inequalities (3.4), (3.6), (3.7), (3.8) there follows

$$\int_0^T \sigma(t)\varphi(t)\, dt + q\Phi(T) + \tfrac{1}{2}\xi^2(T) \leq Cu\xi_1 + q\Phi_0 + \tfrac{1}{2}\gamma u^2.$$

Referring now to (1.1c) the initial value σ_0 of $\sigma(t)$ tends to zero with $\|x_0\| + |\zeta_0| = u$. Since $\Phi(\sigma)$ is a continuous positive function of σ and vanishes for $\sigma = 0$ one may take u so small that $q\Phi_0 < \gamma v$, where v is a given positive quantity. Hence the above inequality yields the following two special cases:

(3.9)
$$\int_0^T \sigma(t)\varphi(t)\, dt < Cu\xi_1 + \tfrac{1}{2}\gamma u^2 + \gamma v.$$

Then if $\xi_1 = \xi(T_1)$ and since we may take $T = T_1$, and also because $\Phi(T) \geq 0$:

(3.10)
$$f(\xi_1) = \xi_1{}^2 - 2Cu\xi_1 - \gamma(u^2 + 2v) \leq 0.$$

Let ξ_1', ξ_1'', be the roots of $f = 0$. Since $\xi_1'\xi_1'' = -(u^2 + 2v) \leq 0$, the roots are of opposite sign and (3.10) requires that ξ_1 be between

96

them. Since $\xi_1 > 0$ it must be below the largest root or

$$\xi_1 < Cu + \sqrt{(C^2 + \gamma)u^2 + 2v}.$$

Since this upper bound of $|\xi(t)|$ for $0 \leq t \leq T$ is independent of T we conclude at once that for all $t \geq 0$:

$$(3.11) \qquad |\xi(t)| < Cu + \sqrt{(C^2 + \gamma)u^2 + 2v}.$$

Since ξ_1 is bounded we also have from (3.9) that

$$(3.12) \qquad \int_0^{+\infty} \sigma(t)\varphi(t)\,dt < \infty$$

that is: the integral is bounded.

Note that the bounds in both cases depend solely upon the initial values x_0 and ξ_0.

Going back to (2.1) we have

$$\int_0^t X(t - \tau)b\varphi(\tau)\,d\tau = \int_0^t X(t - \tau)b\dot{\xi}(\tau)\,d\tau$$

$$= X(t - \tau)b\xi(\tau)\Big]_{\tau=0}^{\tau=t} + \int_0^t \frac{dX(t - \tau)}{d\tau}b\xi(\tau)\,d\tau$$

$$= b\xi(t) - \xi_0 X(t)b + \int_0^t \frac{dX(t - \tau)}{dr}b\xi(\tau)\,d\tau.$$

Referring again to (2.1) the quasi-exponential property of $X(t)$, $\dot{X}(t)$ and (3.11) we obtain

$$(3.13) \qquad \|x(t)\| < C(u + \xi_1), \qquad C > 0.$$

In view of (3.11) and (3.13) we conclude that given $\varepsilon > 0$, one may select $\eta > 0$ such that if $u < \eta$ then $\|x(t)\| + |\xi(t)| < \varepsilon$ for all $t \geq 0$. In other words *the origin is stable for the system* (1.1).

To complete the proof of Popov's first theorem we still need:

(3.14). *Every solution* $(x(t), \xi(t))$ *of* (1.1) *tends to the origin* $x = 0$, $\xi = 0$ *as* $t \to +\infty$, *and this whatever the admissible function* $\varphi(\sigma)$.

As a preliminary step we require:

(3.15) *Both* $\sigma(t)$ *and* $\varphi(t) \to 0$ *as* $t \to +\infty$.

The boundedness of $\|x(t)\|$ and $|\xi(t)|$, coupled with (1.1c) already show that $\sigma(t)$ is bounded. Since $\varphi(\sigma)$ is continuous and $\varphi(0) = 0$, $\varphi(t)$ is likewise bounded. From (1.3b) and the boundedness of $\|x\|$ and $\varphi(t)$ follows that $\dot\sigma(t)$ is likewise bounded. Hence one may select an $M > 0$ such that $|\sigma(t)|$ and $|\dot\sigma(t)| < M$ for all $t \geq 0$. Suppose now that (3.15) does not hold for σ. There exists then a $\delta > 0$, and a divergent positive sequence $t_1 < t_2 < \ldots$ such that $|\sigma(t_k)| > \delta$ for all k. We may actually assume that $t_k - t_{k-1} > \delta/M$, $t_1 > \delta/2M$ and we will have

$$|\sigma(t)| = \left|\sigma(t_k) + \int_{t_k}^t \dot\sigma(\tau)\,d\tau\right| > |\sigma(t_k)| - |M(t - t_k)| > \delta - \tfrac{1}{2}\delta = \tfrac{1}{2}\delta.$$

Since $\varphi(\sigma)$ is continuous and $\varphi(0) = 0$ if and only if $\sigma = 0$, for $M > |\sigma| > \tfrac{1}{2}\delta$ we will have $|\varphi(\sigma)| > R > 0$. Hence if $t_N \leq T < t_{N+1}$, necessarily

$$\int_0^T \varphi(t)\sigma(t)\,dt = \int_0^T |\varphi(t)| \cdot |\sigma(t)|\,dt < \frac{R\delta^2}{4M} \cdot N \to \infty$$

with T. Since this contradicts (3.12), $\sigma(t) \to 0$ and so does $\varphi(t)$.

PROOF OF (3.14). Since $X(t)$ is quasi exponential in the sense that all its terms are, $\|x(t)\| \to 0$ as a consequence of (2.1), of $\varphi(t) \to 0$ and of property III of §2. Referring now to (1.1c) since $\|x(t)\| \to 0$, $\sigma(t) \to 0$ and $\gamma \neq 0$, $\xi(t)$ also $\to 0$. This completes the proof of (3.14) and likewise of Popov's first theorem.

§4. The Generalized Liapunov Function of Popov

In his work Popov considered a more general Liapunov function than the one of the previous chapters. Before attacking the proof of Popov's second theorem it will be profitable to discuss this generalization. Its general type is: quadratic in x, σ plus $\beta\Phi(\sigma)$, i.e.:

$$V(x, \sigma) = x'Bx + \alpha\sigma^2 + \sigma f'x + \beta\Phi(\sigma).$$

This function may immediately be put in the form

$$V = x'Bx + \alpha(\sigma - c'x)^2 + \beta\Phi(\sigma) + \sigma f'x.$$

Then

$$-\dot V = x'Cx + \beta\rho\varphi^2 + 2d_0'x\varphi + 2\alpha\gamma\sigma\varphi - \frac{d}{dt}(\sigma f'x) =$$

$$d_0 = Bb - (\tfrac{1}{2}\beta A'c + \alpha\gamma c),$$

$$A'B + BA = -C.$$

98

The ε method. Upon making a substitution $x \to \varepsilon^p x$, $\sigma \to \varepsilon^q \sigma$, $\varphi \to \varepsilon^r \varphi$, $q + r$ even (to preserve $\sigma\varphi > 0$), V or $\dot{V}$ is turned into a polynomial $P(\varepsilon)$. Let $\lambda\varepsilon^s$ be its lowest degree term. We shall then write $P \doteq \lambda\varepsilon^s$, and P will have the sign of $\lambda\varepsilon^s$ for ε small.

Now

$$\frac{d}{dt}(\sigma f'x) = (x'A'c - \rho\varphi)f'x + \sigma f'(Ax - \varphi b).$$

Hence the substitution

$$x \to \varepsilon x, \qquad \sigma \to \sigma, \qquad \varphi \to \varepsilon^2 \varphi$$

yields if $f \neq 0$:

$$\dot{V} \doteq -\varepsilon\sigma f'Ax.$$

Since A is stable it is nonsingular. Hence if $f \neq 0$ likewise $\sigma f'Ax \neq 0$ for x arbitrary and $\sigma \neq 0$. Hence the sign of $\dot{V}$ for ε small is then that of $\varepsilon\sigma f'Ax$, i.e. it may be $+$ or $-$ according to the sign of ε. Since this is ruled out necessarily $f = 0$.

Thus finally (with repetition and to keep everything together)

$$(4.1) \qquad V = x'Bx + \alpha(\sigma - c'x)^2 + \beta\Phi(\sigma),$$

$$(4.2) \qquad -\dot{V} = x'Cx + \beta\rho\varphi^2 + 2d_0'\varphi x + 2\alpha\gamma\sigma\varphi,$$

$$(4.3) \qquad A'B + BA = -C,$$

$$(4.4) \qquad d_0 = Bb - (\tfrac{1}{2}\beta A'c + \alpha\gamma c).$$

(4.5) *If absolute stability is to be determined by V of* (4.1) *positive definite one requires that* $\alpha \geqq 0$, $\beta \geqq 0$, $\alpha + \beta > 0$.

Let $\alpha \neq 0$. The substitution $x \to \varepsilon x, \sigma \to \sigma, \varphi \to \varepsilon^3 \varphi$ yields $V \doteq \alpha\sigma^2$, hence $\alpha > 0$.

Let $\beta \neq 0$. Then the substitution $x \to \varepsilon^2 x$, $\sigma \to \varepsilon^2 \sigma$, $\varphi \to \varphi$ yields $V \doteq \varepsilon^2 \beta\Phi(\sigma)$, and since $\Phi > 0$ one must have $\beta > 0$.

If both $\alpha, \beta = 0$, $V = 0$ for $x = 0$ and $\sigma \neq 0$, hence $\alpha + \beta > 0$.

To sum up we are left with the following two types of Liapunov functions:

The Lurie-Postnikov function.

$$(4.6) \qquad V = x'Bx + \beta\Phi(\sigma)$$

99

with

$$-\dot{V} = x'Cx + \beta\rho\varphi^2 + 2d'\varphi x$$

$$d = Bb - \tfrac{1}{2}\beta A'c; \qquad A'B + BA = -C.$$

The Popov function.

(4.7) $\qquad V = x'Bx + \alpha(\sigma - c'x)^2 + \beta\Phi(\sigma)$

(4.8) $\qquad -\dot{V} = x'Cx + \beta\rho\varphi^2 + 2d_0'x\varphi + 2\alpha\gamma\sigma\varphi$

$$d_0 = Bb - (\tfrac{1}{2}\beta A'c + \alpha\gamma c), \qquad A'B + BA = -C,$$

together with property (4.5).

§5. Proof of Popov's Second Theorem

Let us modify, with Kalman, Popov's expression in (1.7) through replacing $(1 + i\omega q)$ for some $q \geq 0$ by $2\alpha\gamma + i\omega\beta$ for some nonnegative pair α, β such that $\alpha + \beta > 0$ (α and β do not vanish simultaneously). For $\alpha \neq 0$ the two expressions are clearly equivalent as far as (1.7) goes. However the new expression for $\alpha = 0$ corresponds to q very great in (1.7). The modified Popov inequality is:

(5.1) $\qquad P(\alpha, \beta, \omega) = \beta\gamma + \operatorname{Re}\{(2\alpha\gamma + i\omega\beta)c'A_{i\omega}^{-1}b\} \geq 0$

for all real ω and some pair α, β such that

(5.1a) $\qquad\qquad \alpha \geq 0, \qquad \beta \geq 0, \qquad \alpha + \beta > 0.$

Thus Popov's first theorem reads now: $P \geq 0$, under (5.1a) is a sufficient condition for absolute stability of the system (1.1).

To prove Popov's second theorem we must show that for the function V of (4.7), the double property V and $-\dot{V}$ both positive definite for every admissible φ implies (1.7) for some $q \geq 0$. We shall show, as does Popov, that *it implies* (5.1) *with* α, β *the same constants as in* (4.7).

If a real bilinear form $u'Fu > 0$ for $u \neq 0$ we will write $F > 0$ as if it were a quadratic form. We will require presently the property:

(5.2) *Let u be allowed complex vector values. Then $F > 0$ and the property* $\operatorname{Re} u*Fu > 0$ *for* $u \neq 0$ *are equivalent.*

Here, if $u = u_1 + iu_2$ then $\operatorname{Re} u * Fu = u_i'Fu_1 + u_2'Fu_2 > 0$ for u_1, u_2 not both zero if $F > 0$. Conversely $\operatorname{Re} u * Fu > 0$ for $u \neq 0$ (complex) yields $F > 0$ for u real and $\neq 0$.

Regarding the theorem itself, absolute stability has already led to the proof of (4.5) which is (5.1a). Regarding (5.1) itself, begin with

$$-\dot{V} = -2x'B(Ax - b\varphi) + 2\alpha\gamma\varphi(\sigma - c'x) - \beta\varphi[c'(Ax - b\varphi) - \gamma\varphi] > 0.$$

Hence by (5.2):

(5.3)
$$\mathrm{Re}\{-2x * B(Ax - b\varphi) + 2\alpha\gamma\bar{\varphi}(\sigma - c'x)$$
$$-\beta\bar{\varphi}[c'(Ax - b\varphi) - \gamma\varphi]\} > 0.$$

This inequality is the starting point of the proof.

By definition

$$i\omega E = A + A_{i\omega}.$$

As already observed $A_{i\omega}^{-1}$ exists for all real ω and so the preceding relation yields

$$i\omega A_{i\omega}^{-1}b = A \cdot A_{i\omega}^{-1}b + b.$$

The hypothesis $b = 0$ is unrealistic since it means that the control is not operating. We assume then $b \neq 0$. As a consequence $m(i\omega) = A_{i\omega}^{-1}b \neq 0$ for all ω. Upon substituting in (5.3) $x = -m$, $\varphi = \mu\sigma$, $\mu > 0$ and $\sigma = 1/\mu$; the inequality must hold since it must hold for all complex x, real σ and all admissible φ (in particular for $\varphi = \mu\sigma$). Thus we find

$$\mathrm{Re}\left\{-2m * Bi\omega m + 2\alpha\gamma\left(\frac{1}{\mu} + c'm\right) + \beta[(c'i\omega m) + \gamma]\right\} > 0.$$

Since $m * Bm$ is real $\mathrm{Re}\, i\omega m * Bm = 0$. Hence

(5.4)
$$\frac{2\alpha\gamma}{\mu} + \beta\gamma + \mathrm{Re}\{(2\alpha\gamma + i\omega\beta)c'A_{i\omega}^{-1}b)\} = \frac{2\alpha\gamma}{\mu} + P(\alpha, \beta, \omega) > 0$$

for all real ω. Since the sum must be positive for arbitrarily large positive μ, if $\alpha \neq 0$ we must have $P \geq 0$, while if $\alpha = 0$ (and $\gamma \neq 0$) we require $P > 0$, all this for all real ω. Thus the Popov inequality (5.1) holds, with α, β the same constants as in V. This proves the theorem.

§6. Comparisons

It is interesting to compare what may be accomplished by our comparatively simple methods using the Liapunov–Popov function (4.7) and the earlier type (4.5).

From the function (4.5) one obtained the inequality of (II):

(F_i) $$\rho > d'C^{-1}d,$$

where in reference to the system (1.1)

$$d = Bb - \tfrac{1}{2}A'c.$$

Passing now to the function (4.8) since $\alpha \geq 0$ and $\sigma\varphi > 0$ for $\sigma \neq 0$, we see that to have $-\dot{V}$ positive definite it is sufficient that the quadratic form in x, φ:

$$W = x'Cx + \rho\varphi^2 + 2d_0'\varphi x$$

be positive definite. The same reasoning as for the proof of (F_i) yields the inequality

(6.1) $$\rho > d_0'C^{-1}d_0.$$

Let for the present $\alpha\gamma = u$, and set

$$\psi(u) = d_0'C^{-1}d_0 = \lambda u^2 - 2\mu u + v,$$

$$d_0 = d - \alpha\gamma c, \qquad \lambda = c'C^{-1}c, \qquad \mu = c'C^{-1}d, \qquad v = d'C^{-1}d,$$

One must bear in mind that u must be ≥ 0.

The right-hand side of (6.1), compared with that of (F_i) contains the additional parameter u and we may dispose of it to optimize the inequality (6.1). To be precise the least value of ρ afforded by (F_i) is

$$\rho_m = d'C^{-1}d,$$

while the least value $\rho_m{}^*$ corresponding to (6.1) is to be obtained as the positive minimum of $\psi(u)$ for $u \geq 0$. One must then discuss this minimum. If one finds that $\rho_m > \rho_m{}^*$ the Liapunov–Popov function V will have been proved more advantageous, if not, the earlier function may as well be used.

Observe now that $c = 0$ would mean that the feedback variable σ is independent of the system variable x. Since this is entirely unrealistic and uninteresting, one may assume that the vector $c \neq 0$. Since $C > 0$, hence also $C^{-1} > 0$, the coefficient $\lambda > 0$. It follows that the minimum of $\psi(u)$ occurs for $u = \mu/\lambda$. However this minimum is only admissible if $\mu > 0$. If $\mu \leq 0$ the minimum of $\psi(u)$, for $u \geq 0$ occurs at $u = 0$. We discuss separately the two possibilities.

102

(a) $\mu > 0$. The minimum ψ_m of $\psi(u)$ occurs for $u = u_m = \mu/\lambda$ and its value is

$$\psi_m = v - \frac{\mu^2}{\lambda} = \frac{v\lambda - \mu^2}{\lambda} = -\frac{\delta}{\lambda}$$

where δ is the discriminant of the quadratic $\psi(u)$. That is

$$\delta = (c'C^{-1}d)^2 - (c'C^{-1}c)(d'C^{-1}d).$$

In order to have $\rho_m^* = \psi_m$, the latter must be positive and so one must have $\delta < 0$. Thus if $\delta > 0$ one can only have ρ_m^* arbitrarily small.

At all events since $v = \rho_m$ we have

$$\rho_m^* = \rho_m - \frac{\mu^2}{\lambda}.$$

Hence the Liapunov–Popov function V is certainly more advantageous if $\delta < 0$ and $\mu > 0$, that is $c'C^{-1}d > 0$.

If $\delta > 0$ and $d \neq 0$ we have $\rho_m > 0$ and ρ_m^* arbitrarily small, hence again the Liapunov–Popov function is more advantageous. On the other hand whenever $d = 0$, one cannot claim any advantage for it.

(b) $\mu \leq 0$. This time $u_m = 0$ and so $\rho_m = v = \rho_m^*$. Hence no advantage is afforded by the Liapunov–Popov function.

Application. Consider the standard example (III, §2) under the assumptions that b, c have no zero components, and also that C corresponds to optimum. In all cases for optimum

$$\alpha_h = \mu_h \left| \frac{\lambda_h c_h}{b_h} \right|$$

and

$$C^{-1} = \text{diag}\left(\frac{1}{\alpha_1}, ..., \frac{1}{\alpha_n}\right).$$

Recall that here

$$\sigma = (A'c)'x - \rho\xi.$$

If one assumes that some λ_h are complex one must replace quadratic by hermitian forms and then

$$\mu = \tfrac{1}{2}(c^*C^{-1}d + d^*C^{-1}c) = \text{Re } c^*C^{-1}d.$$

103

Hence since $A = \mathrm{diag}(\lambda_1,..., \lambda_n)$:

$$\mu = \sum \mathrm{Re}\, \bar{c}_h \cdot \frac{1}{\alpha_h}\left(\left(\frac{\alpha_h b_h}{\mu_h}\right) + \lambda_h c_h\right)$$

$$= \sum \left(\mathrm{Re}\, \frac{b_h \bar{c}_h}{\mu_h} - \left|\frac{b_h c_h}{\lambda_h}\right|\right).$$

If this quantity is positive the Liapunov–Popov form will offer a definite advantage, otherwise this is doubtful. For instance if every λ_h is real so that $\lambda_h = -\mu_h < 0$, and if every product $b_h c_h > 0$ one finds $\mu = 0$ and one cannot affirm that the advantage rests with the Liapunov–Popov form.

§7. On the Function $G(z)$ as Transfer Function

Take the system (2.3) and apply to it the Laplace transformation. There results the relation, in which $\hat{x}$, $\hat{\sigma}$, $\hat{\varphi}$, denote the Laplace transforms of x, σ, φ:

$$\text{(a)} \quad z\hat{x} = A\hat{x} - b\hat{\varphi}(t)$$

(7.1)

$$\text{(b)} \quad z\sigma = c'Ax - \rho\hat{\varphi}(t)$$

From (7.1a) there follows $\hat{x} = -A_z^{-1}b\hat{\varphi}$ and hence from (7.1b)

$$(7.2) \qquad z\sigma = -(c'AA_z^{-1}b + \rho)\hat{\varphi}.$$

In view of $A = zE - A_z$ there follows $z\sigma = -z(c'A_z^{-1}b + c'b + \rho)\hat{\varphi}$ and finally

$$\hat{\sigma} = -\left(c'A_z^{-1}b + \frac{\gamma}{z}\right)\hat{\varphi} = -G(z)\hat{\varphi}.$$

Thus $G(z)$ is the transfer function from $-\varphi$ to σ. If we denote this transfer function by $T(z)$ then Popov's inequality (1.7) may be written

$$\mathrm{Re}\{(1 + i\omega q)T(i\omega)\} \geqq 0.$$

This provides a link between this inequality and standard (linear) "transfer" technique.

104

§8. Direct Control

The system to be dealt with is (1.1) but with $\gamma = 0$, or

(8.1) $$\dot{x} = Ax - b\varphi(\sigma), \qquad \sigma = c'x.$$

Take a more general V function than in (IV, §1), namely,

(8.2) $$V = x'Bx + \beta\Phi(\sigma)$$

hence with

(8.3) $$-\dot{V} = x'Cx + 2d'x\varphi(\sigma) + c'b\varphi^2(\sigma)$$

$$A'B + BA = -C, \qquad d = Bb - \tfrac{1}{2}\beta A'c.$$

Passing now to Popov's theorems the proof of the first is directly applicable. Since $\gamma = 0$ it reads:

(8.4) ***Popov's first theorem for a direct control.*** *A sufficient absolute stability condition is the inequality.*

(8.4a) $$P(\omega) = \mathrm{Re}\{(1 + i\omega q)c'A_{i\omega}^{-1}b\} \geqq 0$$

for some $q \geqq 0$ and all real ω.

As regards Popov's second theorem we know from (IV, §1) that $-\dot{V}$ is not positive definite in x and φ.

§9. Conclusion

The special theoretical and even practical importance of Popov's contribution is that in looking for absolute stability conditions it has made it possible to replace the search for a full matrix: B or C of (II) by that of a mere number $q \geqq 0$ which may be determined from a graph (see §1). This applies also to the developments of the next chapter.

Chapter 8

SOME FURTHER RECENT CONTRIBUTIONS

In the present chapter we continue the treatment of absolute stability of the indirect control system of (VII, §1), and notably still assume $\gamma > 0$. Let $P(\alpha, \beta, \omega)$ and $V(x, \sigma)$ be the Popov and Liapunov functions of (VII, 4.6, 4.7). By strengthening a theorem of Yacubovich [3] (our main lemma below) Kalman [2] succeeded in completing essentially Popov's second theorem to a n.a.s.c., his "sufficiency" part however requiring a further strong restriction. Our proposed more modest task is to prove, following largely Kalman, that $P > 0$ plus a very simple restriction yield n.a.s.c. to have V and $-\dot{V}$ both positive definite and also absolute stability. While our treatment is thus relatively simple, it is only fair to say that most of the difficulties in Kalman's treatment were caused by weakening ">" to "≧" ($P \geqq 0$, $\dot{V} \leqq 0$). However our simpler attack will suffice to give the reader an idea of that of Kalman. In the last section we discuss the effect of restricting the admissible class of characteristic functions by an inequality $0 < \varphi(\sigma)/\sigma \leqq \kappa$.

While we shall lean almost entirely upon the work of Kalman, the notations are those of the previous chapters. For convenience the reader may use the following transfer table:

106

Notations of the text:	A	b	c	ξ	ρ	γ
Notations of Kalman:	F	g	h	$-\xi$	γ	ρ

§1. Controllability and Observability

While these concepts have appeared here and there in the literature before Kalman, he has had the great merit of giving them explicit form, content and application. See notably Kalman [2] and Kalman and associates [1].

Roughly speaking a controlled system is *completely controllable* (c.c.) if one cannot decompose it into two systems with the control operating in only one of the systems; otherwise it is merely partially controllable or simply noncontrollable. Controllability operates through the vector b. Something similar takes place regarding observability and the vector c appearing in the expression of σ. The latter is the feedback or "visible" effect of the control, hence observable.

Without going into further detail we adopt the following explicit definition (Kalman): The pair (A, b) is *completely controllable* (c.c.) whenever the vectors b, Ab, A^2b,..., $A^{n-1}b$ are linearly independent. The pair (c', A) is *completely observable* (c.o.) whenever $(A'; c)$ is c.c. As a matter of fact the important property of independence of the vectors $A^k b$ has been considered by many authors. See for example LaSalle [3, Introduction and p. 15].

Our main purpose in the present chapter is the proof of the fundamental theorem of §6. Now from a very general theory developed by Kalman [2, No. 12] one may infer:

(1.1) *There is no loss of generality in assuming that the pair (A, b) is completely controllable and the pair (c', A) is completely observable.*

The reduction of our system to this type and also its justification will be carried out in the next section.

Recall this well-known property: if the characteristic equation of the matrix A is

$$(1.2) \qquad \lambda^n + a_n\lambda^{n-1} + \cdots + a_1 = 0$$

then A satisfies the matrix equation

$$(1.3) \qquad A^n + a_nA^{n-1} + \cdots + a_1E = 0.$$

107

This property is usually expressed as: *the matrix satisfies its own characteristic equation.*

If (A, b) is c.c., (1.2) is the equation of lowest degree (up to a constant factor) satisfied by A: it is also its *minimal* equation. In fact if A satisfied an equation of degree $p < n$, e.g.,

$$A^p + a_p' A^{p-1} + \cdots + a_1' E = 0$$

then the $p + 1$ vectors b, Ab,..., $A^p b$, would not be independent, contradicting the complete controllability of (A, b).

(1.4) *The property of complete controllability of (A, b) is independent of the choice of coordinates.*

For the change of coordinates $x \to Px$ yields $A \to P^{-1}AP$, $b \to P^{-1}b$. Hence the set of vectors $S = \{A^k b\}$, $0 \le k < n$ goes into $S_1 = \{P^{-1}A^k b\}$. Since P and P^{-1} are nonsingular, linear independence of one of the sets implies that of the other, hence (1.4) follows.

We shall also require this property:

(1.5) *A n.a.s.c. for complete controllability of the pair (A, b) is that if a vector x is such that $x' e^{At} b = 0$ for all t then $x = 0$.*

It will be convenient to utilize orthogonality. Two vectors u, v are orthogonal if $u'v = v'u = 0$. As is well known and readily proved, a n.a.s.c. for the existence of a vector $u \ne 0$ orthogonal to n vectors $v_1,..., v_n$ is that the v_h be linearly dependent.

Observe also that (1.3) yields

$$A^{k+n}b + a_n A^{k+n-1}b + \cdots + A^k b = 0$$

whatever k. Hence the vectors $A^k b$ all depend linearly upon the set S defined above.

We come now to the actual proof of (1.5).

NECESSITY. Let (A, b) be c.c. and let $x' e^{At} b = 0$ for all t. Upon differentiating k times and setting $t = 0$ there follows in particular $x' A^k b = 0$, $0 \le k < n$. Since x is orthogonal to the linearly independent vectors of S, necessarily $x = 0$. This proves necessity.

SUFFICIENCY. Let the property of (1.5) hold. As a consequence if $x' A^k b = 0$ whatever k then $x' = 0$. Since these $A^k b$ depend linearly upon the vectors of S, if x is orthogonal to all the vectors of S alone then $x = 0$. Hence S consists of linearly independent vectors. Hence (A, b) is c.c.: sufficiency is proved and so is (1.5).

§2. Reduction of the System to One with a Completely Controllable Pair (A, b) and Completely Observable Pair (c', A)

The above title states our objective. However to describe the reduction process a convenient notation is needed.

Let $A = \text{diag}(A_1,..., A_r)$ and let n_h be the order of A_h so that $\Sigma n_h = n$. If f is any vector let f^h denote the vector whose components of order $n_1 + n_2 + \cdots + n_{h-1} + s$, $1 \leqq s \leqq n_h$, are the same as those of f and the rest zero. Thus $f = \Sigma f^h$.

Method of reduction. The only manner in which the pair (A, b) will affect later arguments is through expressions of type $f'A^{-1}b$, where under a transformation of coordinates $x \to Px$, f behaves like $c : f \to P'f$, so that $f'A_z^{-1}b$ is unchanged. Note that *this implies freedom in changing coordinates*.

Now the following operation does not modify $f'A_z^{-1}b$: If

$$A = \text{diag}(A_1,..., A_r)$$

then

$$f'A_z^{-1}b = \sum f^{h'}A_{hz}^{-1}b^h.$$

Hence if $b^h = 0$ the summand $f^{h'}A_{hz}^{-1}b^h = 0$ whatever f. Hence A_h and related coordinates will not affect any later argument and so they may be suppressed. That is, one may freely replace A, as far as the sequel goes, by $\text{diag}(A_1,..., A_{h-1}, A_{h+1},..., A_r)$. This may also be justified in the following manner. Since $b^h = 0$ the vector x^h satisfies $\dot{x}^h = A_h x^h$ which is a system with constant matrix and *no control*: control-neutral. Since A is stable so is A_h. Hence the solutions $x^h(t)$ all $\to 0$ naturally as $t \to +\infty$ and so one may as well disregard A_h and related coordinates.

An analogous process may be applied in the following case. Let A_h be a block matrix: $A_h = C_h(\lambda_h)$, such as occurs in the Jordan normal form (IX, §1). Let b^h be such that its coordinate of order $v = n_1 + \cdots + n_h$ is zero. In view of the form of A_h the components f_v, b_v, of f, b enter in $f'A_z^{-1}b$

solely through the expression

$$\frac{f_v(z - \lambda)^{v-1}b_v}{|A_{hz}|} = 0.$$

As above, then, one may suppress the coordinate x_v and components f_v, b_v without affecting anything. In particular $C(\lambda)$ will merely be replaced by a similar block but of order one unit less. This operation may of course be repeated.

Our reduction consists, then, in the suppression of certain submatrices and terms and allowable coordinate transformations, i.e. in which real points are always represented by certain conjugate pairs of coordinates. These operations will not affect the nature of the Jordan normal form.

A final remark referring to the submatrices A_h in the diagonal form. The statement: (A_h, b^h) is c.c. merely means that the vectors $A_h{}^s b^h$, $0 \leq s < n_h$ are linearly independent.

We now proceed with our process of reduction. As we may assume that A is in the Jordan normal form it is convenient to consider first a single block matrix.

Matrix $A = C(\lambda)$, $\lambda \neq 0$. Since one may assume that the preceding reductions have already been applied one may assume that $b \neq 0$ and also that its component $b_n \neq 0$. We prove:

Property α. *Under the preceding assumptions the pair* $(C(\lambda), b)$ *is completely controllable.*

The proof is a consequence of the following two properties:

Property β. *One may choose coordinates such that* $C(\lambda)$ *is unchanged but* b' *becomes the vector* $(0,..., 0, 1)$.

Property γ. *If* $b' = (0,..., 0, 1)$ *the pair* $(C(\lambda), b)$ *is completely controllable.*

PROOF OF β. The transformation

$$y_1 = c_1 x_1 + \cdots + c_n x_n$$
$$y_2 = c_1 x_2 + \cdots + c_{n-1} x_n$$
$$\cdot \quad \cdot \quad \cdot$$
$$y_n = c_1 x_n$$

is nonsingular provided that $c_1 \neq 0$ and it preserves the block property

110

of A. Choose it so that b has the prescribed form. This yields the system in the c_h:

$$c_1 b_h + c_2 b_{h+1} + \cdots + c_{n-h+1} b_n = 0, \qquad h < n,$$
$$c_1 b_n \qquad\qquad\qquad\qquad = 1.$$

The determinant is $\pm b_n{}^n \neq 0$, hence there is a unique solution. Since $c_1 = 1/b_n$, the transformation of coordinates $x \to y$ is legitimate, and as it does not modify the form of A, property β follows.

PROOF OF γ. We will show that if $x' e^{At} b = 0$ for all t then $x = 0$. Thus γ will be a consequence of (1.5). Let $e^{At} = (\beta_{ik})$. Then

$$x' e^{At} b = \sum x_h \beta_{hn}.$$

Now an elementary calculation yields

$$\beta_{hn} = e^{\lambda t} \cdot \frac{t^{n-h}}{(n-h)!}$$

Hence

$$x' e^{At} b = e^{\lambda t} \sum_{k=1}^{n} \frac{x_k t^{n-k}}{(n-k)!}.$$

The assumption implies that the polynomial of the sum is identically zero. Hence every $x_k = 0$, $x = 0$ and γ, hence also α, follows.

General pair (A, b). We may take A in the Jordan normal form and without blocks whose $b^h = 0$ or last component $b_v = 0$. Take again a definite characteristic root λ with two blocks $C'(\lambda)$, $C''(\lambda)$ of orders p, q with p least for such blocks so that $p \leq q$. Let x_h', $h = 1, 2, ..., p$ and x_k'', $k = 1, 2, ..., q$ denote the associated coordinates. One may assume that their b^j, e.g. b' and b'' are both of type $(0, ..., 0, 1)$. Apply the coordinate transformation $x_{q-p+1}'' \to x_{q-p+1}'' - x_1', ..., x_q'' \to x_q'' - x_p'$. As a consequence the types of $C'(\lambda)$ and $C''(\lambda)$ will be unchanged but b'' will be replaced by zero. Hence $C''(\lambda)$ may be suppressed. Upon repeating this operation as many times as necessary, A will still be in normal form but with distinct characteristic roots for distinct blocks and all the b^h of type $(0, ..., 0, 1)$. We must now show that when this happens (A, b) is c.c.

Write simply $A = \operatorname{diag}(A_1, ..., A_r)$ where $A_h = C_h(\lambda_h)$.

Referring again to (1.5) one merely needs to show that if

(2.1) $$x' e^{At} b = 0$$

111

for all t then $x = 0$. Now (2.1) is equivalent to this:

$$x^{h'} e^{A_h t} b^h = 0, \qquad h = 1, 2,..., r$$

for all t implies that every $x^h = 0$. As this property is a consequence of the complete controllability of (A_h, b^h), (2.1) is proved. Hence finally (A, b) is c.c. This completes the reduction.

Complete observability of (c', A). Let generally T denote the preceding operations on A which lower its order n and alone affect c.c. of (A, b) or c.o. of (c', A).

Now starting with the initial A, to achieve c.c. of (A, b) may have required to apply operations T from A to A_1 of order $n_1 < n$ and associated b^1, c^1 with (A_1, b^1) c.c. If $(c^{1'}, A_1)$ is not c.o. an analogous (dual) procedure will yield A_2 of order $n_2 < n_1$ and $(c^{2'}, A_2)$ c.o., etc. The process must clearly stop, e.g. with an $A_0 = 0$: final system control neutral, which is not realistic, and therefore ruled out, or with $A_0 \neq 0$, hence (in evident notations) with (A_0, b^0) c.c. and $(c^{0'}, A_0)$ c.o. Thus the reduction of (1.1) will have been achieved. We will say briefly that (A_0, b^0, c^0) is c.c. and c.o.

Comparison of initial and reduced systems. Let all the designations of (VII, §1) be reserved for the reduced system. In view of the reduction process the initial system, conveniently assumed of dimension $n + p$, has the general form

(2.2)
$$
\begin{aligned}
&\text{(a)} \quad \dot{x} = Ax + A_2 y - b\varphi(\sigma) \\
&\text{(b)} \quad \dot{y} = A_1 y \\
&\text{(c)} \quad \dot{\xi} = \varphi(\sigma) \\
&\text{(d)} \quad \sigma = c'x - \gamma\xi.
\end{aligned}
$$

Here y is a p vector, the matrices A_1, A_2 are $p \times p$ and $n \times p$ matrices and the triple (A, b, c) is c.c. and c.o.

We are now faced with two distinct problems—mathematical and practical. As a *mathematical* problem one must deal with the system (2.2) as it stands and not suppress any coordinates: no reduction may be made. *Practically* however the situation is quite different. Let b_0 denote the vector like b corresponding to (2.2). This vector and the analog c_0 are design elements. If b_0, c_0 have been chosen so that the parts b, c alone are $\neq 0$, it means that one has considered the role of the vector y as immaterial as regards control. At this point one must recall that the vectors x, y merely represent deviations from certain initial system coordinate vectors (see the Introduction). Thus the deviation y has been considered, by design, as immaterial. Hence it may reasonably be neglected. That is, one may replace y by zero and what is then left of the system (2.2) is really the system (VII, 1.1) but with (A, b, c) c.c. and c.o. This assumption will be made throughout the rest of the chapter.

§3. A Special Form for Systems with Completely Controllable Pair (A, b)

When the pair (A, b) is completely controllable the following vectors

$$e_n = b$$

$$e_{n-1} = (A + a_n E)b$$

$$e_{n-2} = (A^2 + a_n A + a_{n-1} E)b$$

$$\cdot \quad \cdot \quad \cdot$$

$$e_1 = (A^{n-1} + a_n A^{n-2} + \cdots + a_2 E)b,$$

where the a_n are as in (1.2), are linearly independent and hence they constitute a base e. The effect of A on this base is given by

$$Ae_n = e_{n-1} - a_n e_n$$

$$Ae_{n-1} = e_{n-2} - a_{n-1} e_n$$

(3.2)
$$\cdot \quad \cdot \quad \cdot$$

$$Ae_1 = \qquad - a_1 e_n.$$

Hence if we adopt e as a base for coordinates, A will become

(3.3)
$$A = \begin{pmatrix} 0 & 1 & & & & \\ & 0 & 1 & & & \\ & \cdot & & \cdot & \cdot & \cdot & \cdot & & \cdot \\ & \cdot & & & \cdot & \cdot & \cdot & \cdot & & \cdot \\ -a_1 & -a_2 & \cdot & \cdot & \cdot & \cdot & -a_n \end{pmatrix}$$

and b will be represented by

(3.4)
$$b' = (0, 0, \ldots, 0, 1).$$

It will turn out later that this type of matrix A and vector b will alone need to concern us.

Given the importance in the sequel and also, e.g., in Popov's relation of the expression $c'A_z^{-1}b$, it is convenient to calculate it for the above pair (A, b). One must first calculate the vector $A_z^{-1}b = v$.

If $A_z^{-1} = (\alpha_{jk})$, the components of the vector v are $\alpha_{1n}, \alpha_{2n},..., \alpha_{nn}$, that is, the last column of A_z^{-1}. This column consists of the cofactors of the last row of

$$A_z = \begin{pmatrix} z & -1 & & & \\ & z & -1 & & \\ & & & -1 & \\ a_1 & a_2 & \cdots & (a_n + z) \end{pmatrix}$$

divided by $|A_z|$. The cofactors are readily found to be $1, z,..., z^{n-1}$. Hence if c_h are the components of c we have

(3.5)
$$c'A_z^{-1}b = \frac{c_1 + c_2 z + \cdots + c_n z^{n-1}}{|A_z|}.$$

In particular

(3.6)
$$c'A_{i\omega}^{-1}b = \frac{c_1 + c_2(i\omega) + \cdots + c_n(i\omega)^{n-1}}{|A_{i\omega}|}.$$

Since no particular properties of the vector c have been utilized in deriving (3.5) we may state:

(3.7) *If f is any vector with components f_h then*

(3.7a)
$$f'A_z^{-1}b = \frac{f_1 + f_2 z + \cdots + f_n z^{n-1}}{|A_z|}.$$

§4. Main Lemma (Yacubovich and Kalman)

This lemma is at the root of the fundamental theorem to follow (§6). It comes closest to a result of Yacubovich [3, Theorem 3], and the necessity proof below differs very little from that of Yacubovich. However, the sufficiency proof, which is the more difficult part, is essentially inspired

114

by the same part of the proof of Kalman's main lemma [2], perhaps the most original feature of his treatment.

(4.1) **Main lemma.** *Given the stable matrix A, a symmetric matrix $D > 0$, vectors $b \neq 0$ and k, and scalars $\tau \geq 0, \varepsilon > 0$, then a n.a.s.c. for the existence of a solution as a matrix B (necessarily >0) and vector q of the system*

$$\text{(a)} \quad A'B + BA = -qq' - \varepsilon D$$

(4.2)

$$\text{(b)} \quad Bb - k = \sqrt{\tau}q$$

is that ε be small enough and that the Kalman relation

(4.3)
$$\tau + 2\operatorname{Re} k' A_{i\omega}^{-1}b > 0$$

be satisfied for all real ω.

As in (VII, §5) set $m(i\omega) = A_{i\omega}^{-1}b$. Thus $m(i\omega)$ is a complex vector function of ω. With this notation one may also write (4.3) in the form

(4.4)
$$\tau + k'm + m^*k > 0.$$

Notice now the identity

$$A_{i\omega}^*B + BA_{i\omega} = -(A'B + BA).$$

If one multiplies the right-hand side by $A_{i\omega}^{-1}b$ and the left-hand side by $b'A_{i\omega}^{*-1}$, then take account of (4.2) there follows

(4.5)
$$m^*Bb + b'Bm = m^*qq'm + \varepsilon m^*Dm.$$

This relation will be used at once.

We come now to the proof of the lemma proper.

PROOF OF NECESSITY. In (4.5) replace Bb from (4.2). As a consequence

(4.6)
$$2\operatorname{Re} k'm = |q'm|^2 - 2\sqrt{\tau}\operatorname{Re} q'm + \varepsilon m^*Dm.$$

Moreover if one considers D as a hermitian matrix then $D_1 = A_{i\omega}^{*-1}DA_{i\omega}^{-1}$ is the hermitian matrix deduced from D by the change of coordinates $x \to A_{i\omega}^{-1}x$. Hence $D_1 > 0$ like D, and so since $b \neq 0$

$$\delta = \varepsilon b'D_1 b = \varepsilon m^*Dm > 0.$$

Upon applying (4.6) there follows

(4.7)
$$2\operatorname{Re} k'm = |q'm|^2 - 2\sqrt{\tau}\operatorname{Re} q'm + \delta.$$

If $q'm = \lambda + i\mu$, (4.7) yields

$$\tau + 2\operatorname{Re} k'm = (\lambda - \sqrt{\tau})^2 + \mu^2 + \delta > 0$$

which is (4.3). This proves necessity.

PROOF OF SUFFICIENCY. We first establish a preliminary result.

(4.8) *If u is a real constant vector such that* $\operatorname{Re} u'm(i\omega) = 0$ *whatever ω then $u = 0$.*

Suppose that $u \neq 0$ and let u_h be its components. Referring to (3.7) we have

$$\psi_0(z) = u'm(z) = \frac{u_1 + u_2 z + \cdots + u_n z^{n-1}}{|A_z|}.$$

This function has the following properties:

(a) It is rational in z and not identically zero.

(b) Its poles are among the characteristic roots of A and hence, since A is stable, they are all to the left of the complex axis.

(c) Since the numerator of $\psi_0(z)$ is of smaller degree than the denominator there is at least one such pole.

(d) $\psi_0(z)$ takes only complex values on the complex axis.

It follows that $\psi(z) = i\psi_0(iz)$ is a rational function of z which takes only real values on the real axis and hence it is real. Moreover it has one or more poles and they are all to one side of the real axis. Now if α is such a pole so is $\bar{\alpha}$ and the two are separated by the real axis. This contradiction shows that $u = 0$.

Passing now to the sufficiency proof proper since both

(4.9) $$\kappa(\omega) = m^*k + k'm, \qquad \pi(\omega) = m^*Dm$$

are real rational functions of ω with numerators of degree $\leq n - 1$ and denominator of degree n, both $\to 0$ as $\omega \to +\infty$. Furthermore they are continuous for ω finite. Hence they have finite upper and lower bounds. Let μ be the upper bound of $\pi(\omega)$ and v the lower bound of $\kappa(\omega)$. Since $\pi(\omega) > 0$ for all finite ω, we have $\mu > 0$. Hence

$$\tau + m^*k + k'm - \varepsilon m^*Dm \geq \tau + v - \varepsilon\mu.$$

Moreover owing to (4.3) $\tau + v > 0$. Hence if one chooses $\varepsilon < \frac{1}{2}[(\tau + v)/\mu]$, we have

(4.10) $$\tau + m^*k + k'm - \varepsilon m^*Dm > 0.$$

§4. MAIN LEMMA (YACUBOVICH AND KALMAN)

Let now $\psi(z) = |A_z|$. Thus $\psi(z)$ is a real polynomial with leading coefficient unity. Now the left hand side of (4.10) may be written

$$\tau + k'm(i\omega) + m^*(i\omega)k - \varepsilon m^* Dm = \frac{\xi(i\omega)}{\psi(i\omega)}$$

$$= \frac{\xi(i\omega)\psi(-i\omega)}{\psi(i\omega)\psi(-i\omega)} = \frac{\eta(i\omega)}{\psi(i\omega)\psi(-i\omega)}.$$

Here $\eta(z)$ is a polynomial of degree $2n$ with leading coefficient τ. Since $\eta(i\omega)$ is real and >0 (4.10), $\eta(i\omega) = \eta_1(\omega^2), \eta_1$ a real polynomial without real roots. Hence

$$\eta_1(\omega^2) = \theta(i\omega)\theta(-i\omega),$$

where $\theta(z)$ is a real polynomial. Since the leading coefficient of $\theta(z)\theta(-z)$ is τ, that of $\theta(z)$ is $\sqrt{\tau}$, and the degree of $\theta(z)$ is n. By division and since the leading coefficient of $\psi(z)$ is unity

$$\frac{\theta(z)}{\psi(z)} = \frac{v(z)}{\psi(z)} + \sqrt{\tau}$$

where $v(z)$ is a polynomial of degree at most $n - 1$. If $q_1, q_2, ...,$ are its (real) coefficients, define q by

$$q' = (-q_1, ..., -q_n).$$

Once q is known one obtains the matrix B from (4.2) and as we know $B > 0$.

The above leads to the relation

$$(4.11) \quad \tau + k'm + m^*k - \varepsilon m^* Dm = \left(\frac{v(i\omega)}{\psi(i\omega)} - \sqrt{\tau}\right)\left(\frac{v(-i\omega)}{\psi(-i\omega)} - \sqrt{\tau}\right).$$

Referring on the other hand to (2.2) and recalling the meaning of m we have

$$\frac{v(i\omega)}{\psi(i\omega)} = -q'm.$$

117

Hence the relation (4.11) yields for the chosen q

$$k'm + m^*k - \varepsilon m^* Dm = (m^* q - \sqrt{\tau})(q'm - \sqrt{\tau}) - \tau$$

$$= m^* q q'm - \sqrt{\tau}(q'm + m^* q)$$

$$= -(m^* Bb + b'Bm) - \varepsilon m^* Dm - \sqrt{\tau}(q'm + m^* q),$$

the last step by (4.5). Hence whatever ω:

$$m^*(Bb - k - \sqrt{\tau}q) + (Bb - k - \sqrt{\tau}q)'m$$

$$= 2\,\text{Re}(Bb - k - \sqrt{\tau}q)'m = 0.$$

Since the vector in parentheses is real it must vanish, showing that (4.2b) is satisfied. That is, a solution (B, q) has been found for the system (4.2). Thus sufficiency of (4.3) is proved. This completes the proof of (4.1).

§5. Liapunov–Popov Function and Popov Inequality

Their connection has already been emphasized (VII, §§4, 5) and we recall that the function $V(x, \sigma)$, the related $\dot{V}$ and the Popov inequality are

(5.1) $\qquad V(x, \sigma) = x'Bx + \alpha(\sigma - c'x)^2 + \beta\Phi(\sigma);$

(5.2) $\qquad -\dot{V} = x'Cx + \beta\rho\varphi^2(\sigma) + 2d_0'x\varphi(\sigma) + 2\alpha\gamma\sigma\varphi(\sigma);$

$\qquad d_0 = Bb - (\tfrac{1}{2}\beta A'c + \alpha\gamma c).$

(5.3) $\qquad P(\alpha, \beta, \omega) = \beta\gamma + \text{Re}\{(2\alpha\gamma + i\omega\beta)c'A_{i\omega}^{-1}b\} \geqq 0.$

We also state the following generalization of the Lurie problem resembling one due to Kalman:

Generalized Lurie problem. *To find n.a.s.c. to assure absolute stability by means of the function $V(x, \sigma)$ of (5.1), i.e., through V and $-\dot{V}$ both positive for all x, σ not both zero, and all admissible characteristic $\varphi(\sigma)$.*

This problem is solved by the fundamental theorem (§6).

Reduction of Kalman's relation (4.3) to Popov's (5.3). At first glance, although quite similar, they seem to deal with two different problems.

118

Actually by a specialization of the constant k appearing in (4.3) one obtains (5.3).

Referring to the expression (5.2) of $\dot{V}$ let

$$k = Bb - d_0 = \tfrac{1}{2}\beta A'c + \alpha\gamma c$$

and in Kalman's relation let $\tau = \beta\rho = \beta(\gamma + c'b)$. As a consequence (4.3) yields

(5.4) $$\beta\rho + 2\,\text{Re}\{(\tfrac{1}{2}\beta c'A + \alpha\gamma c')A_{i\omega}^{-1}b\} > 0.$$

The bracket may be written

$$\tfrac{1}{2}\beta c'(i\omega E - A_{i\omega})A_{i\omega}^{-1}b + \alpha\gamma c'A_{i\omega}^{-1}b$$
$$= -\tfrac{1}{2}\beta c'b + \tfrac{1}{2}\beta c'i\omega A_{i\omega}^{-1}b + \alpha\gamma c'A_{i\omega}^{-1}b.$$

Since $\rho - c'b = \gamma$, (5.4) reduces to (4.3). That is, with the substitutions indicated for the constants (5.3) reduces to (4.3).

§6. Fundamental Theorem

With the lemma behind us we are in position to prove:

(6.1) **Theorem.** *N.a.s.c. for both V and $-\dot{V}$ of §5 to be positive definite for all (x, σ) and choice of an admissible φ are the Popov-Kalman inequality* (4.3) *together with*

(6.2)
  (a) $\alpha \geqq 0,\quad \beta \geqq 0,\quad \alpha + \beta > 0;$

  (b) $\tau > 0\quad\text{or}\quad \tau = 0,\quad d_0 = 0,\quad \alpha > 0.$

When these properties are satisfied the system (VII, 1.1) *is absolutely stable.*

(6.3) REMARK. It is quite instructive to compare the above theorem and the apparently similar theorem (II, 2.11). The earlier theorem refers to the Lurie–Postnikov function V and in its conditions there enter the matrix C and the control parameters b, c, ρ. In the present theorem the V function is the more general Popov type and in its conditions there enter merely the scalars α, β and the control parameters. The difference is due, of course, to the appearance of the powerful Popov condition.

PROOF OF NECESSITY. The necessity of (6.2a) has already been proved. Regarding (6.2b) let $\tau \neq 0$. Then the substitution $x \to \varepsilon x, \varphi \to \varphi, \sigma \to \varepsilon^2\sigma$

119

yields $-\dot{V} \doteq \tau\varphi^2$ and so one must have $\tau > 0$. Suppose now $\tau = 0, d_0 \neq 0$. Then the same substitution yields $-\dot{V} \doteq 2\varepsilon\varphi(\sigma)\, d_0'x$: the sign of $\dot{V}$ changes with that of ε hence one must have $d_0 = 0$. Then however $\alpha \neq 0$, hence $\alpha > 0$, since otherwise $\dot{V} = 0$ for $x = 0, \sigma \neq 0$. Thus (6.3b) must hold.

Consider now separately $\tau > 0$ and $\tau = 0$.

I. $\tau > 0$. One may then write

$$(6.4) \qquad -\dot{V} = x'(C - qq')x + (\sqrt{\tau}\varphi + q'x)^2 + 2\alpha\gamma\sigma\varphi,$$

where q is defined by (4.2b). Choose $\|x\|$ large, ε small, $\sigma_0 \neq 0$ and fixed and $\sigma = \varepsilon^2\sigma_0$, $\varphi(\sigma) = \mu\varepsilon^2\sigma_0$ with μ such that $\varepsilon^2\mu\sigma_0\sqrt{\tau} + q'x = 0$ if $q'x \neq 0$, and any $\mu > 0$ if $q'x = 0$. Then $-\dot{V} \doteq x'(C - qq')x$, hence $C - qq' = D > 0$. Thus (4.2) holds, hence by the lemma (4.3) is satisfied. Thus necessity is proved in this case.

II. $\tau = 0, d_0 = 0, \alpha > 0$. Taking $\sigma = 0$ and any x, we have $-\dot{V} \doteq x'Cx$, hence $C > 0$ and so by (6.2c) $B > 0$. Since $d_0 = 0$, (4.2) holds with $q = 0$, $\varepsilon = 1$. Therefore the Popov–Kalman inequality is satisfied, and necessity is completely proved.

PROOF OF SUFFICIENCY. Since (4.3) holds given $D > 0$ there exists $\varepsilon > 0$ such that the system (4.2) has a solution (B, q). Note that

$$C = \varepsilon D + qq' > 0,$$

hence also $B > 0$.

It is convenient now to deal separately with V and $\dot{V}$. Take first V. If $\alpha = 0$ then $\beta > 0$ and so $V > 0$ for $x \neq 0$ or if $x = 0$ for $\sigma \neq 0$. Hence V is positive definite for all x, σ and admissible φ. On the other hand if $\alpha \neq 0$ the sum of the first two terms in (5.1) is a positive definite quadratic form in x, σ and the conclusion is the same.

Consider now $\dot{V}$. If $\tau \neq 0$ (5.2) becomes

$$-\dot{V} = \varepsilon x'Dx + (\sqrt{\tau}\varphi(\sigma) + q'x)^2 + 2\alpha\gamma\sigma\varphi(\sigma).$$

Hence the sum of the first two terms is positive definite for all x, σ and admissible φ and so $-\dot{V}$ has the same property. If $\tau = 0$ then $d_0 = 0$, $\alpha > 0$. Hence (5.2) reduces to

$$-\dot{V} = x'Cx + 2\alpha\gamma\sigma\varphi(\sigma).$$

Since $C > 0$ and $\alpha > 0$ this expression is likewise positive definite for all x, σ and admissible φ.

120

Since both V and $-\dot{V}$ are, always, positive definite for all x, σ and admissible φ, sufficiency is proved.

PROOF OF ABSOLUTE STABILITY. All that is now needed is to show that $V \to \infty$ with $\|x\| + |\sigma|$ (Barbashin–Krassovskii complement, IX, 4.7). Owing to $B > 0$ and property III of (I, §1) for φ this is true if $\alpha = 0$ since then $\beta > 0$. It holds also when $\alpha > 0$ since the first two terms in the expression (5.1) of V make up a positive definite quadratic form in x and σ.

§7. A Recent Result of Morozan

It is interesting to return to the inequality (F_i) of (II, §2) for the number ρ. In our present notations and since c *loc. cit.* is here $A'c$, and hence k for $\alpha = 0$, $\beta = 1$ is $\frac{1}{2}A'c$, we have

(F_i) $\qquad\qquad \rho > (Bb - k)'C^{-1}(Bb - k).$

At a meeting in Kiev in September 1961, the author raised the question of finding the minimum of ρ for all choices of the basic matrix $C > 0$. This question has recently been solved by Morozan [1]. We have however all that is required to obtain an answer here. Namely when $\alpha = 0$, taking $\beta = 1$, (4.3) yields

$$\rho + 2\operatorname{Re} k' A_{i\omega}^{-1} b > 0.$$

Here, however, $k = \frac{1}{2}A'c$. Hence

$$\rho + \operatorname{Re}(c'A \cdot A_{i\omega}^{-1}b) > 0.$$

From $A_{i\omega} = i\omega E - A$ there follows

$$\rho - c'b + \operatorname{Re} i\omega c' A_{i\omega}^{-1} b > 0.$$

Since this last inequality must hold for all real ω we find

(7.1) $\qquad\qquad \rho > c'b + \sup_{\omega} \operatorname{Im} \omega c' A_{i\omega}^{-1} b.$

Owing to the n.a.s.c. of the fundamental theorem the right-hand side represents the true least value of ρ. Owing no doubt to differences in notations this result does not coincide with that of Morozan.

§8. Return to the Standard Example

In the preceding chapter we have already made a comparison between the two types of function $V(x, \sigma)$: (VII, 4.6), form of Lurie–Postnikov ($\alpha = 0$), and Popov form (VII, 4.8), ($\alpha > 0$). We return to the same question here and arrive at comparisons based upon rather simple estimates obtained from Popov's inequality.

For simplicity the discussion will be restricted to the case $\beta > 0$. Thus Popov's inequality may be written

$$(8.1) \qquad \gamma + \operatorname{Re}(\delta + i\omega)c'A_{i\omega}^{-1}b > 0$$

where $\delta = 2\alpha\gamma/\beta$. In our earlier notation $m(i\omega) = c'A_{i\omega}^{-1}b = S_1(\omega) + iS_2(\omega)$ one may write (8.1) as

$$(8.2) \qquad \gamma > \omega S_2 - \delta S_1,$$

which is to hold for some $\delta \geqq 0$ and all real ω.

It is evident that one may take $\beta = 1$. Then $\delta = 0$ corresponds to the Lurie–Postnikov type of function $V(x, \sigma)$ and $\delta > 0$ to the Popov generalization.

Since (8.1) is independent of the choice of coordinates (a fact readily established) we may assume that $A = \operatorname{diag}(\lambda_1,..., \lambda_n)$. As a consequence

$$A_{i\omega}^{-1} = -\operatorname{diag}\left(\frac{1}{\lambda_1 - i\omega},..., \frac{1}{\lambda_n - i\omega}\right),$$

and therefore

$$c'A_{i\omega}^{-1}b = -\sum\frac{b_h c_h}{\lambda_h - i\omega}.$$

The relation (9.1) will only yield rather simple estimates when all the λ_h are real. We confine our attention to this case. Thus $\lambda_h = -\mu_h < 0$. Hence

$$c'A_{i\omega}^{-1}b = \sum\frac{b_h c_h}{\mu_h + i\omega}.$$

Hence

$$S_1 = \sum\frac{b_h c_h \mu_h}{\mu_h^2 + \omega^2}, \qquad S_2 = -\omega\sum\frac{b_h c_h}{\mu_h^2 + \omega^2}$$

Taking into account the relation $\rho = \gamma + c'b$ we obtain from (8.1):

$$(8.3) \qquad \rho > \sum \frac{\mu_h(\mu_h - \delta)b_h c_h}{\mu_h^2 + \omega^2}.$$

It is now necessary to distinguish between the signs of the products $b_h c_h$. Let $b_h' c_h'$ denote the positive products and μ_h' their μ_h, and $b_h'' c_h''$, μ_h'' the negative products and their μ_h. Suppose also that

$$\mu_1' \leqq \mu_2' \leqq \cdots \leqq \mu_p', \qquad \mu_1'' \leqq \mu_2'' \leqq \cdots \leqq \mu_q''.$$

Now it is clear that (8.3) will hold if one merely preserves the $b_h' c_h'$, chooses $\delta = \mu_1'$ and $\omega = 0$. Let

$$\rho_P' = \sum b_h' c_h' \left(1 - \frac{\mu_r'}{\mu_h'}\right).$$

Similarly set

$$\rho_P'' = -\sum b_h'' c_h'' \left(\frac{\mu_q''}{\mu_h''} - 1\right).$$

It is evident that if ρ_P is the least of the numbers ρ_P', ρ_P'' then ρ_P is a suitable lower bound for the number ρ.

Now let us see what one obtains as lower bound for ρ from our inequality (F_i). Referring to (II, 5) its vector c, now written c_0, has for components $-\mu_h c_h$. Hence the inequality (F_i) yields here

$$\rho > \sum b_h' c_h' = \rho_m.$$

It is clear that *if the products $b_h c_h$ are not all negative $\rho_P < \rho_m$, hence the Popov type of Liapunov function, i.e. with a suitable $\alpha > 0$, is then more advantageous than the Lurie–Postnikov type with $\alpha = 0$ (our earlier type).*

§9. Direct Control

The most interesting direct control of order n is the one which reduces to an indirect control of order $n - 1$ and is fully discussed in (IV, §§6, 7). The state matrix A of the direct control has zero as simple characteristic root. All that we propose to do here is to adapt the theorem of §6 to that case.

In the notations *loc. cit.* the system is

(9.1)
$$\dot{x}_0 = A_0 x_0 - b_0 \varphi(\sigma)$$

$$\dot{\sigma} = g' x_0 - \rho \varphi(\sigma)$$

where A_0 is a stable $(n - 1) \times (n - 1)$ matrix.

One may apply directly the fundamental theorem of §6 under the following identifications: A_0 corresponds to A; x_0 to x, b_0 to b, $g' = c_0' A_0$ to $c'A$, c_0 to c. Here also $\gamma = \rho - c_0' A_0 b_0$. Finally ρ and $\varphi(\sigma)$ have the same meaning as in §6.

§10. Résumé (Indirect Control: $\gamma > 0$)

The variety of results on the Popov expression $P(\alpha, \beta, \omega)$ and the Liapunov function $V(x, \sigma)$ of (5.1) as related to absolute stability, may be summarized as follows:

I. *Popov's first theorem.* A sufficient condition for absolute stability is
(10.1) $P(\alpha, \beta, \omega) \geqq 0$ for some $\alpha, \beta \geqq 0$, $\alpha + \beta > 0$, and all real ω.

II. *Popov's second theorem.* (10.1) is a necessary condition to have absolute stability via V and $-\dot{V}$ positive definite, with α and β the same in P and V.

III. *Kalman's theorem.* (10.1) plus another (complicated) condition is a n.a.s.c. to have absolute stability through $V > 0$, $\dot{V} \leqq 0$, with same α, β in P and V.

IV. *Theorem of §6.* (10.1) with $P > 0$ plus $\beta\rho > 0$ or $\beta\rho = 0$, $d_0 = 0$, $\alpha > 0$ are n.a.s.c. to have absolute stability secured through V and $-\dot{V}$ both positive definite.

V. However, in III and IV the pair (A, b) is assumed completely controllable. In both also a certain theorem of Yacubovich plays a major role.

Suppose now that in the initial system (VII, 1.1) *the pair (A, b) is not completely controllable.* As we have shown in §2, one may choose coordinates, and select a reasonable vector c^2 such that the initial system is replaced by (2.2) together with (2.3) where now (A_1, b) is completely controllable. Popov's first theorem provides a sufficient condition for the absolute stability of the *full system* (2.2, 2.3). *It would evidently be most desirable to prove that* $P \geqq 0$, *supplemented, perhaps, by some simple inequality is also a necessary condition for absolute stability.* Since (2.3) already has this property, it might suffice to obtain this result for a completely controllable pair (A, b). Up to the present, however, this remains an open question.

§11. Complement on the Finiteness of the Ratio $\varphi(\sigma)/\sigma$

Two recent publications led to this complement: (a) a noteworthy paper by Yacubovich [4] in which he deals not only with the restriction in the title but even with a possible isolated function $\varphi(\sigma)$; (b) an extensive monograph by Aizerman and Gantmacher [1] where the restriction in question is accepted throughout. This has induced the author to examine the possible modifications in the results of the chapter presented by the added condition

$$(11.1) \qquad \sigma \neq 0: \qquad 0 < \frac{\varphi(\sigma)}{\sigma} \leqq \kappa, \text{ finite}$$

to our admissible class. As indirect and direct controls proceed along entirely distinct lines, the two cases are separated.

Indirect control. Take

$$V = x'Bx + \alpha(\sigma - c'x)^2 + \beta\Phi(\sigma)$$

and modify $\dot{V}$ by adding and subtracting

$$\lambda(\sigma) = 2\alpha\gamma\left(\sigma - \frac{\varphi(\sigma)}{\kappa}\right)\varphi(\sigma).$$

Thus $\lambda(\sigma) > 0$ for $\sigma \neq 0$, or $\varphi(\sigma) < \kappa\sigma$ and $\lambda(0) = 0$ if $\varphi(\sigma) = \kappa\sigma$. Then

$$-\dot{V} = x'Cx + \tau_0\varphi^2(\sigma) + 2d_0'x\varphi(\sigma) + \lambda(\sigma)$$

$$A'B + BA = -C, \qquad \tau_0 = \tau + \frac{2\alpha\gamma}{\kappa} = \beta\rho + \frac{2\alpha\gamma}{\kappa},$$

$$d_0 = Bb - \tfrac{1}{2}\beta A'c - \alpha\gamma c.$$

Replace now Popov's initial expression by the κ-Popov expression:

$$P(\alpha, \beta, \omega, \kappa) = P(\alpha, \beta, \omega) + \frac{2\alpha\gamma}{\kappa} = \beta\gamma + \frac{2\alpha\gamma}{\kappa} + \text{Re}\{(2\alpha + i\omega\beta)c'A_{i\omega}^{-1}b\}.$$

125

Under the same modifications as before in §5 (expression of k) it is identical with the κ-Kalman expression

$$K(\alpha, \beta, \omega, \kappa) = \tau_0 + 2 \operatorname{Re} k' A_{i\omega}^{-1} b.$$

The new fundamental theorem is:

(11.2) **κ-Theorem for indirect control.** *N.a.s.c., in order that, with V as above, both V and $-\dot{V}$ be positive definite for all x, σ and all κ-admissible functions φ (φ restricted by 11.1) is that the κ-Popov–Kalman inequality:*

$$P(\alpha, \beta, \omega, \kappa) > 0$$

hold for all real ω together with

(11.3) $$\tau_0 > 0.$$

When these properties are satisfied the system is absolutely stable in the sense that φ is restricted by (11.1).

PROOF OF NECESSITY. To prove (11.3) take $\varphi(\sigma) = \kappa\sigma$ so that

$$-\dot{V} = x'Cx + \tau_0\varphi^2 + 2d_0'\varphi x.$$

For $x = 0$ and $\tau_0 \neq 0$ then $-\dot{V} = \tau_0\kappa^2\sigma^2$, hence $\tau_0 > 0$. On the other hand $\tau_0 = 0$ is ruled out since then $-\dot{V}$ cannot be positive definite in x, σ. Thus (11.3) holds. Write now

$$-\dot{V} = x'(C - qq')x + (\sqrt{\tau_0}\varphi + q'x)^2.$$

Take any $x \neq 0$ and determine σ by $\sqrt{\tau_0}\kappa\sigma = -q'x$. As a consequence $-\dot{V} = x'(C - qq')x > 0$ for all $x \neq 0$. Hence $C - qq' = D > 0$. Thus all the necessary conditions of the main lemma are fulfilled with $\tau = \tau_0$. Hence the κ-Popov–Kalman inequality holds and necessity is proved.

PROOF OF SUFFICIENCY. It is practically the same as in (6.3) save that one need not consider $\tau_0 = 0$.

The proof of absolute stability with the κ restriction added is the same as in §6, with the modification

$$-\dot{V} = \varepsilon x'Dx + (\sqrt{\tau_0}\varphi(\sigma) + q'x)^2 + 2\alpha\gamma\left(\sigma - \frac{\varphi(\sigma)}{\kappa}\right)\varphi(\sigma)$$

which does not affect the proof.

126

Direct control. This time the system is

(11.4) $$x' = Ax - b\varphi(\sigma), \qquad \sigma = c'x.$$

As Liapunov function take

(11.5) $$V(x) = x'Bx + \beta\Phi(\sigma),$$

hence

(11.6) $$-\dot{V}(x) = x'Cx + 2d'x\varphi(\sigma) + \tau\varphi^2(\sigma)$$

$$A'B + BA = -C, \qquad d = Bb - \tfrac{1}{2}\beta A'c, \qquad \tau = \beta c'b.$$

Actually the role of $\dot{V}$ is really played by the function

$$W(x) = -\dot{V} - \delta\left(\sigma - \frac{\varphi(\sigma)}{\kappa}\right)\varphi(\sigma)$$

$$= x'Cx + 2(d - \tfrac{1}{2}\delta c)'x\varphi + \left(\tau + \frac{\delta}{\kappa}\right)\varphi^2$$

where $\delta > 0$.

In the presence of the restriction (11.1) the adequate theorem here is:

(11.7) **κ-*Theorem for a direct control.*** *Sufficient conditions for V positive definite as a function of x for all admissible functions φ satisfying (11.1) and W as a quadratic form in x and φ (unrestricted) is the κ-Popov inequality.*

(11.8) $$P(\delta, \beta, \omega, \kappa) = \frac{\delta}{\kappa} + \operatorname{Re}\{(\delta + i\omega\beta)c'A_{i\omega}^{-1}b\} > 0$$

for some $\beta \neq 0$, some positive δ, and all real ω. When these conditions are fulfilled both V and $-\dot{V}$ are positive definite and we have absolute stability.

REMARK. This theorem does not really differ in substance from a theorem of Aizerman and Gantmacher [2, p. 78]. They give conditions referring to a Liapunov function V with the property that if V is positive definite under the restriction (11.1) then W is positive definite in x, φ *without* restriction.

The proof of sufficiency can be carried out by a slight modification of the argument of the sufficiency proof of our fundamental theorem (§6). It is also obvious that when the given conditions hold

$$-\dot{V} = W + \delta\left(\sigma - \frac{\varphi(\sigma)}{\kappa}\right)\varphi(\sigma)$$

is positive definite in x (arbitrary) and φ (restricted by 11.1). Absolute stability is then established as in §6.

Chapter *9*

MISCELLANEOUS COMPLEMENTS

§1. The Jordan Normal Form for Real or Complex Matrices

In the sections on vectors and matrices the notations are those of (II, §1).

In connection with the reduction to the normal form, it is particularly convenient to have recourse to bases for vector spaces.

Changing slightly our previous point of view, consider the symbol x to represent a certain vector v in the coordinate system x. Thus the transformation of coordinates $y = Px$, P nonsingular, does not change the vector v but merely provides a new representation of v in the y coordinate system. In other words the vector v is independent of the coordinate system but is merely endowed with various representations in various coordinate systems.

Let e_h denote the vector which in the x system has coordinates δ_{hk} (Kronecker deltas). The system $\{e_h\}$ is a base in the sense that the vector v may be written uniquely

$$(1.1) \qquad v = e_1 x_1 + \cdots + e_n x_n$$

(it is convenient to put the x_j after the factors e_j).

A useful convention is to think of the e_h as the components of a one-column matrix (vector) designated by e. Then in an evident sense,

128

under our matrix conventions (1.1) may be written

(1.2) $$v = e'x.$$

Now if one applies the transformation $x = Py$ one finds

$$v = e'Py = f'y, \qquad f' = e'P$$

or equivalently $f = P'e$. Thus the coordinate transformation $x = Py$ is associated with the "base transformation" $f = P'e$.

We have already observed on repeated occasions that if in the differential equation

$$\dot{x} = Ax, \qquad A \text{ constant,}$$

one applies the above transformation of coordinates, the system is replaced by

$$\dot{y} = A_0 y, \qquad A_0 = P^{-1}AP.$$

That is, the effect on the matrix A is to replace it by the *similar* also called *equivalent* matrix A_0. The relationship is written with the standard equivalence symbol $A_0 \sim A$. Furthermore A_0 is any matrix $\sim A$.

In order to describe the Jordan normal form we will utilize two special designations. We will write $A = \mathrm{diag}(A_1,..., A_r)$, where the A_h, are, like A, square matrices and follow one another in the principal diagonal as if they were elements, the rest being zero matrices. We shall also write

$$C_s(\lambda) = \begin{pmatrix} \lambda & 1 & & & & & \\ & \lambda & 1 & & & & \\ & & \cdot & \cdot & \cdot & \cdot & \cdot \\ & & \cdot & \cdot & \cdot & \cdot & \cdot \\ & & & & & \lambda & 1 \\ & & & & & & \lambda \end{pmatrix}$$

where $C_s(\lambda)$ is $n \times n$ and all missing terms are zero. Actually one may also assume that the diagonal $1, 1,...$ is below the main diagonal.

We now state without proof (for the proof see Lefschetz [1, Appendix I]):

(1.3) **Theorem.** *Every complex matrix A is equivalent in the complex domain (that is by means of a complex transformation matrix P) to a matrix*

$$A_0 = \mathrm{diag}(C_{r_1}(\lambda_1),..., C_{r_s}(\lambda_s))$$

129

where the λ_h are the characteristic roots of A (and also of any matrix $\sim A$), all included, some perhaps repeated. The order of the "blocks" $C(\lambda)$ is immaterial.

The proof *loc. cit.* is based on a systematic selection of base elements, one set e.g. $e_{h1},...,e_{hr_h}$ corresponding to the block $C_{r_h}(\lambda_h)$.

Now when the matrix A is real, the characteristic roots appear in conjugate pairs $\lambda_h, \bar{\lambda}_h$. It is also shown *loc. cit.* that if $C_{rh}(\lambda_h)$ is a block associated with λ_h, then there appears also the block $C_{rh}(\bar{\lambda}_h)$. Moreover the base vector f may be so chosen that if $(f_{h1},...,f_{hr_h})$ is the subbase associated with $C_{r_h}(\lambda_h)$ then one may choose a subbase $(\bar{f}_{h1},...,\bar{f}_{hr_h})$ corresponding to $C_{r_h}(\bar{\lambda}_h)$ as part of f. As a consequence, if the vector v (the point x) is real and if y_j is its coordinate corresponding to f_{hj} then its coordinate corresponding to $\bar{f}_{hj}$ will be $\bar{y}_j$. This is expressed by the statement: real x points will be represented in the complex y coordinates by pairs of conjugate coordinates. Thus the y coordinates may be ordered like this:

$$y_1,..., y_p, \quad \bar{y}_1,..., \bar{y}_p, \quad y_{2p+1},..., y_n$$

where the y_{2p+h} are real and correspond to the blocks with real λ_h.

Let $f_j, \bar{f}_j$ be associated as above to $y_j, \bar{y}_j$. One may replace them in the base vector f by the real elements

$$f_j' = \frac{f_j + \bar{f}_j}{2}, \qquad f_j'' = \frac{f_j - \bar{f}_j}{2i}$$

which are both real. If y_j', y_j'' are the real coordinates corresponding to f_j', f_j'' then identically

$$y_j f_j + \bar{y}_j \bar{f}_j = y_j' f_j' + y_j'' f_j''$$

$$= y_j'\left(\frac{f_j + \bar{f}_j}{2}\right) + y_j''\left(\frac{f_j - \bar{f}_j}{2i}\right).$$

From this follows (since $f_j, \bar{f}_j$ are independent):

$$y_j = \frac{y_j' + iy_j''}{2}, \qquad \bar{y}_j = \frac{y_j' - iy_j''}{2}.$$

By examining the effect on the bases e (real) and f (complex) it is readily found that the transformation matrix P from the real coordinates

x to the complex coordinates y has the form

$$P = \begin{pmatrix} Q \\ \bar{Q} \\ R \end{pmatrix}$$

where Q and $\bar{Q}$ are $p \times n$ matrices and R is a real $q \times n$ matrix,

$$q = n - 2p.$$

Consider a general system

$$\dot{x} = X(x), \qquad X(0) = 0$$

where X is e.g. of class C^1 in a neighborhood Ω of the origin. We merely assert that *a change of coordinates $x = Py$ does not affect the stability properties of the origin.* This is readily proved for instance by means of the inequality on p. 20 of LaSalle and Lefschetz [1].

For additional information (especially proofs) of the properties just considered, see the following well-known books: Bellman [1], Gantmacher [1], also in part Lefschetz [1, Appendix I].

We recall the following:

(1.4) **Theorem.** *Every positive definite quadratic [hermitian] form may be reduced by a real [complex] affine transformation of coordinates to the form*

$$x'x = \sum x_h{}^2 \qquad [x^*x = \sum x_h \bar{x}_h].$$

The transformation, for example, for a quadratic form may be made in two steps. A first orthogonal transformation $x \to Px$, $P^{-1} = P'$, reduces the form to

$$\sum \alpha_h x_h{}^2, \qquad \alpha_h > 0.$$

Then the affine transformation $x_h \to x_h/\sqrt{\alpha_h}$ brings it to the required type. We also recall the following property utilized earlier.

(1.5) *If the real symmetric [hermitian] matrix $C > 0$ then likewise C^{-1} is real symmetric [hermitian] and >0.*

The treatment of the hermitian case is the same as the other [with $(\,)^*$ instead of $(\,)'$], so we confine our attention to the real case.

131

Since $C' = C$ we have $C^{-1} = (C')^{-1} = (C^{-1})'$, and so C^{-1} is symmetric. Let now P be an orthogonal transformation reducing C to the diagonal form

$$P^{-1}CP = P'CP = D = \mathrm{diag}(\alpha_1, \ldots; \alpha_n)$$

where every $\alpha_h > 0$. Then

$$D^{-1} = P^{-1}C^{-1}(P')^{-1} = P'C^{-1}(P^{-1})' = P'C^{-1}(P')' = P'C^{-1}P.$$

Since $D^{-1} = \mathrm{diag}(1/\alpha_1, \ldots, 1/\alpha_n)$, we have $D^{-1} > 0$, and since it is the transform of C^{-1} by the orthogonal transformation P, likewise $C^{-1} > 0$.

§2. On a Determinantal Relation

There has occurred in the previous chapters a determinantal relation which we propose to derive in the present section.

Let M be an $(n + 1) \times (n + 1)$ matrix and suppose that

$$M = \begin{pmatrix} N & p \\ q' & \alpha \end{pmatrix}$$

where N is a nonsingular $n \times n$ matrix, p and q are n vectors and α is a scalar. The relation in question is

(2.1) $$|M| = |N|(\alpha - q'N^{-1}p).$$

To prove this relation multiply M (left-hand side) by $\mathrm{diag}(N^{-1}, 1)$. As a consequence

$$\mathrm{diag}(N^{-1}, 1) \cdot M = \begin{pmatrix} E, & N^{-1}p \\ q', & \alpha \end{pmatrix}.$$

Let $N^{-1}p = r$, so that the last matrix is

$$S = \begin{pmatrix} E & r \\ q' & \alpha \end{pmatrix}$$

and

$$|S| = \begin{vmatrix} E & r \\ q' & \alpha \end{vmatrix}.$$

From well-known rules on determinants it is found that r_1 and q_1 appear in the expansion as the product $-q_1 r_1$ and nowhere else. By permuting rows and columns it is seen that similarly q_h and r_h appear in the product $-q_h r_h$ and nowhere else. Hence $|S| = \alpha - q'r$ and from this to the desired relation (2.1) is but a step.

The relation (2.1) may be generalized as follows. Let

$$M = \begin{pmatrix} N & P \\ Q' & R \end{pmatrix}$$

where N is $n \times n$, R is $s \times s$ and P, Q are $n \times s$ matrices, with N non-singular. Then

$$|M| = |N|(|R - Q'N^{-1}P|).$$

The proof is practically the same as for (2.1).

§3. On Liapunov's Matrix Equation

Take the n vector equation

$$(3.1) \qquad \dot{x} = Ax$$

where A is a constant stable matrix. Let $V(x) = x'Bx$ be a quadratic form. Its time derivative along the paths of (3.1) is

$$(3.2) \qquad \dot{V} = \frac{\partial V}{\partial x} \cdot Ax = -W(x) = -x'Cx$$

where we have the Liapunov relation

$$(3.3) \qquad A'B + BA = -C.$$

This relation has frequently occurred in the previous chapters, the following property being repeatedly utilized:

133

(3.4) *If the matrix A is stable and C is any given matrix* > 0 *then* (3.3) *has a unique solution B and B* > 0.

The same property holds for a matrix A with some complex characteristic roots, but still stable, save that (3.3) is replaced by

$$(3.5) \qquad A^*B + BA = -C$$

where B, C are now hermitian and > 0. There is so little difference between the treatments of the two cases that it will suffice to deal with (3.4). As a matter of fact, the result has often been dealt with in the literature (see for example LaSalle and Lefschetz [1; 3, §17]) but we believe that our present attack is particularly direct and simple.

Observe first that a transformation of coordinates $x = Py$ will replace (3.1) by

$$\dot{y} = A_0 y, \qquad A_0 = P^{-1}AP$$

and $x'Bx$, $x'Cx$ by $y'B_0 y$, $y'C_0 y$, where $B_0 = P'BP$, $C_0 = P'CP$. Hence (3.3) yields

$$P'A'P'^{-1}P'BP + P'BPP^{-1}AP = -P'CP$$

which is

$$(3.6) \qquad A_0'B_0 + B_0 A_0 = -C_0.$$

Thus (3.3) is unaffected by a transformation of coordinates. Since this transformation may be inverted, it is sufficient to prove the asserted property for (3.6).

Now one may choose the transformation of coordinates so that A_0 is *triangular*, that is, only with zeros above the main diagonal. Indeed the Jordan normal form is already of this form. The terms in the main diagonal are then the characteristic roots of A_0 (the same as those of A). Thus

$$A_0 = \mathrm{diag}(\lambda_1,..., \lambda_n) + D,$$

where $D = (d_{jk})$ is triangular with zeros in the main diagonal. Let b_{jk}^0, c_{jk}^0 be the terms of B_0, C_0. The equation (3.6) gives rise to a set of relations

$$(3.7) \qquad (\lambda_j + \lambda_k)b_{jk}^0 = -c_{jk}^0 + \delta_{jk}(..., b_{hk},...)$$

where δ_{jk} is a linear form in the b_{hk} such that $h + k > j + k$ with coefficients in the d_{rs}. Since every Re $\lambda_j < 0$, the system (3.7) can be solved step by step by an induction downward from $j + k = 2n$, and the solution is unique. Hence (3.6) has a unique solution B_0 and (3.3) has a unique solution B. If B is that solution (3.3) yields

$$B'A + A'B' = -C' = -C.$$

Hence, B' is likewise a solution of (3.3) and so $B' = B$. The treatment of (3.5) is the same with A' replaced by A^*.

REMARK. There are two noteworthy special cases, repeatedly considered in the previous chapters as the standard example, when the solutions of (3.3) or (3.5) are especially simple.
(a) The λ_h are all real, $\lambda_h = -\mu_h < 0$, and $A = \text{diag}(-\mu_1,..., -\mu_n)$.
(b) Some λ_h are complex, $\text{Re }\lambda_h = -\mu_h < 0$ and $A = \text{diag}(\lambda_1,..., \lambda_n)$.
In the case (a) the relation (3.1) yields at once

$$(\mu_j + \mu_k)b_{jk} = c_{jk},$$

hence

(3.8) $$b_{jk} = \frac{c_{jk}}{\mu_j + \mu_k}.$$

In the case of (b) (3.2) yields

$$(\bar{\lambda}_j + \lambda_k)b_{jk} = -c_{jk},$$

hence now

(3.9) $$b_{jk} = \frac{-c_{jk}}{\bar{\lambda}_j + \lambda_k}.$$

We shall now prove:

(3.10) *The unique solution B of* (3.3) *just obtained is* > 0.

Notice that with the earlier result this property is equivalent to this proposition:

(3.11) **Theorem.** (Liapunov). *Given the positive definite quadratic form* $W(x)$, *the partial differential equation* (3.2) *for* $V(x)$ *has a unique solution as a positive definite quadratic form.*

At all events there is a solution $V(x) = x'Bx$ as a quadratic form. Suppose that $V(x)$ is *not* positive definite. If it can take negative values, it is known from Liapunov's instability theorem that the origin must be

135

unstable for the system (3.1). However we know from the form of the solutions that the origin is asymptotically stable. Hence $V(x) \geqq 0$.

Suppose that $V(x_0) = 0$ for some $x_0 \neq 0$. Let γ be the path issued from x_0 at time $t = 0$. Along γ we have $\dot{V} = -W(x) < 0$, hence $V(x)$ will become and remain <0 along γ. Since this contradicts the result already obtained $V(x) > 0$ for $x \neq 0$, hence $B > 0$. Thus both (3.10) and (3.11) are proved.

We have actually all the elements for the proof of the following noteworthy proposition.

(3.12) **Theorem.** *A necessary and sufficient condition for the stability of the real matrix A is that there exist two real matrices $B, C > 0$ which satisfy the relation* (3.3).

Necessity has already been proved. To prove sufficiency let λ be a characteristic root of A. There exists then a vector $u \neq 0$ such that $Au = \lambda u$. Since A is real $A' = A^*$. Thus $u^*A^* = \bar{\lambda}u^*$. Now from (3.6) follows

$$u^*(A^*B + BA)u = 2(\lambda + \bar{\lambda})u^*Bu < 0.$$

Since $B > 0$ this implies $\lambda + \bar{\lambda} = 2 \operatorname{Re} \lambda < 0$ and so A is stable.

§4. Liapunov and Stability

As Liapunov's theory has been referred to many times in the previous chapters, we shall give a rapid résumé of it insofar as it applies to an autonomous system

$$(4.1) \qquad\qquad \dot{x} = X(x), \qquad X(0) = 0.$$

Let S_R denote the spherical region $\|x\| < R$ and H_R the boundary sphere of the region.

The system (4.1) is supposed to be of class C^1 in a certain region S_A.

Liapunov defines the origin as: stable *for* (4.1) *whenever given any* $0 < \varepsilon < A$ *there corresponds to it a* $0 < \eta(\varepsilon) \leqq \varepsilon$ *such that if $x(t)$ is a solution whose initial position $x_0 = x(0)$ lies in S_η then $x(t)$ lies in S_ε ever after;*

Asymptotically stable whenever the origin is stable, and furthermore for some ε every solution $x(t)$ as above $\to 0$ as $t \to +\infty$;

Unstable whenever given any $0 < \varepsilon < A$ and no matter what $0 < \eta < \varepsilon$ there is always an $x(t)$ as above reaching H_ε at some time $t > 0$.

The stability theorems of Liapunov given below rest upon this concept: A scalar function $V(x)$ is *positive [negative] definite in the region* S_A whenever $V(x)$ is of class C^1 in S_A, $V(0) = 0$, and $V(x) > 0[<0]$ otherwise in S_A. This implies that

(4.2) $$\dot{V} = \frac{d}{dt}V(x(t))$$

along a solution $x(t)$ of (4.1) in S_A is given by

(4.3) $$\dot{V} = \frac{\partial V}{\partial x} \cdot X.$$

(4.4) **Stability theorem.** *Whenever for some S_A there exists a positive definite function $V(x)$ whose derivative $\dot{V}$ along the paths of (4.1) is $\leqq 0$ in S_A then the origin is stable.*

(4.5) **Asymptotic stability theorem.** *Whenever $\dot{V}$ is actually negative definite in S_A the origin is asymptotically stable.*

(4.6) **Instability theorem.** *If there exists a positive definite function $V(x)$ in S_A, of class C^1 there, whose derivative $\dot{V}$ along the paths is likewise positive and of class C^1 outside the origin in S_A then the origin is unstable. Moreover (not explicit in the proof but obvious) every H_ε, $\varepsilon < A$, may be reached by any path initiated from a point of S_ε (origin excepted).*

The instability theorem, while not utilized in the previous chapters, will be required in a moment.

For the proofs of the above theorems see LaSalle and Lefschetz [1, p. 57]. (The instability theorem has been stated in less general form than *loc. cit.*, but in a form sufficient for our present purpose.)

(4.7) **The Barbashin–Krassovskii complement to the asymptotic stability theorem** [1]. *In the latter theorem let: (a) $S_A = S_\infty$; (b) $V \to \infty$ with $\|x\|$. Then all solutions tend to the origin.*

A direct proof of this proposition offers no difficulty. However it is interesting to observe that (4.7) is a consequence of the instability theorem *applied to infinity*. This requires a word of explanation.

Let the space of x be *closed at infinity by a single point*. It becomes topologically an n sphere S^n in which one may think of the point at infinity as the north pole N and the origin as the south pole S. The conditions of (4.7) applied to N state that upon defining $W(N) = 0$, then the

137

function $W = 1/V$ is positive definite in any spherical region of center N with a time derivative $\dot{W}$ along the paths which is > 0 in any such region, N excepted. For $\dot{W} = -\dot{V}/V^2 = -W^2 \cdot \dot{V} > 0$ as stated. This is sufficient for the application of the instability theorem: N is unstable and every H_ε, whatever ε, is reachable by any solution outside H_ε. This is precisely the statement of (4.7).

There are closely related investigations by Yoshizawa [1], and also, regarding the "closing at infinite by a point," related contributions of Auslander and Seibert. See notably their paper [1].

In conclusion we recall the following noteworthy

(4.8) **Theorem of LaSalle.** *If the set of points where $V < l$ is bounded for all finite positive l (obvious here) and the locus of points such that $\dot{V} = 0$ contains no other solutions than the origin then the system under consideration for which V is positive definite and $-\dot{V}$ positive semidefinite is asymptotically stable in the large. And, in particular, if this holds for all admissible functions φ we have absolute stability.*

Appendix A

AN APPLICATION OF MULTIPLE FEEDBACK CONTROL

Throughout the present monograph it has been systematically assumed that the system matrix A had no characteristic roots with positive real parts. This is equivalent to assuming at the outset that the initial n vector system

(1) $$\dot{x} = Ax$$

was stable. We shall say that the matrix A is *irregular* whenever it does possess characteristic roots with nonnegative real parts. This includes in particular the case when the system (1) is actually unstable: the precise situation when the action of a control seems most imperative! We shall now prove:

Theorem. *When the matrix A is irregular one may define a multiple feedback control with variables $\sigma_1, \sigma_2,..., \sigma_r$ such that the matrix of the enlarged system $(x, \sigma_1,..., \sigma_r)$ is stable.*

Upon using, for example the reduction to the Jordan normal form, one may assume that

$$A = \text{diag}(A_1, C_1(\lambda_1),..., C_r(\lambda_r))$$

139

where A_1 is stable and the blocks $C_h(\lambda_h)$ are irregular: the λ_h have non-negative real parts. Let q_h be the order of $C_h(\lambda_h)$.

Let also the coordinates be so designated that the system (1) assumes the form

(2) $\qquad \dot{x}' = A_1 x', \qquad \dot{y}^h = C_h(\lambda_h)y^h, \qquad h = 1, 2,..., r.$

Our theorem will be proved if we can show that one may replace the y^h system by an enlarged system with stable matrix. For convenience drop the index h and write the y^h system as

(3) $\qquad\qquad\qquad \dot{y} = C(\lambda)y$

where y is a q vector. Consider the new system

$$\dot{y} = \begin{pmatrix} \lambda & 1 & & & \\ & \lambda & 1 & & \\ & & \cdot & \cdot \cdot \cdot \cdot \cdot \\ & & & & \lambda \end{pmatrix} y + f\sigma$$

$$\dot{\sigma} = g'y + \alpha\sigma,$$

$$f' = (0, 0,..., 0, 1), \qquad g' = (g_1, g_2,..., g_q).$$

Here α and the g_h are constants which are to be so determined that the matrix of (4) be stable.

By referring to (IX, §2) and (VIII, §3), we find at once that the characteristic equation of (4) is

(5) $\qquad (z - \alpha)(z - \lambda)^q - g_q(z - \lambda)^{q-1} - \cdots - g_1 = 0.$

Take any $\mu > 0$. Our purpose will be fulfilled if we can select α and the g_h, so that the above polynomial is $(z - \mu)^{q+1}$. Upon setting $z - \lambda = u$, $\lambda - \alpha = \beta$, $\lambda - \mu = \rho$, this reduces to selecting β and the g_k so that

$$u^{q+1} + \beta u^q - g_q u^{q-1} - \cdots - g_1 \equiv (u + \rho)^{q+1}.$$

Since this choice is always possible and even uniquely so, the theorem is proved.

In the last analysis one will face the following situation: A system in the following variables:

(1) the initial phase n vector x;

(2) the additional variables $\sigma_1, \sigma_2,..., \sigma_r$, one for each block $C_h(\lambda_h)$;

(3) the standard old type feedback variable σ with characteristic $\varphi(\sigma)$ such as studied for example in Chapters II, III, and IV.

The constant matrix A_0 corresponding to x and the σ_h (order $n + r$) is stable and we have a multiple feedback vector with components $(\sigma_1, \sigma_2,..., \sigma_r, \sigma)$.

Once $\sigma_1, \sigma_2,..., \sigma_r$ are introduced we are back to the situations of the text (a single feedback variable σ).

Appendix B

AN EXAMPLE FROM THE THEORY OF NUCLEAR POWER REACTORS
(Kenneth Meyer)

Our theory can be applied to problems outside of control theory. The following problem was studied by Smets [1]. Let the scalar η be the mean neutron density of a nuclear reactor. The neutron density η satisfies an equation

$$\dot{\eta} = k\eta$$

where k, the reactivity, is a function of the state of the reactor.

The reactivity k can be assumed to be a linear function of η and the temperatures $y_1,..., y_n$ of various components of the reactor. For example $y_1, y_2,...$ may be the temperatures of the fuel, coolant etc. Specify $k = k_0 + c'y - \rho\eta$ where k_0 is a scalar constant and $y' = (y_1,..., y_n)$. If one assumes that the heat transfer arises from conduction one may apply Newton's law of cooling to find that y satisfies the equation

$$\dot{y} = Ay - b\eta.$$

In the above equations A, b, c and ρ are as in the text. Let A be non-singular.

142

Critical points. If y, η is a critical point for the above system of equations then

$$Ay - b\eta = 0, \qquad (k_0 + c'y - \rho\eta)\eta = 0$$

or

$$y = A^{-1}b\eta, \qquad \{k_0 + (c'A^{-1}b - \rho)\eta\}\eta = 0.$$

Thus $y_1 = 0, \eta_1 = 0$ and

$$y_2 = A^{-1}b(\rho - c'A^{-1}b)^{-1}k_0, \qquad \eta_2 = (\rho - c'A^{-1}b)^{-1}k_0$$

are the only critical points provided $\rho - c'A^{-1}b \neq 0$. Since $\eta \geq 0$, one must have $\eta_2 \geq 0$.

The point y_1, η_1 corresponds to the reactor when shut down and y_2, η_2 corresponds to the steady state operating point when the reactor is producing power.

Clearly one would want the critical point y_2, η_2 to be asymptotically stable for all y and all $\eta > 0$. Let $\eta_2 \neq 0$ and let us change the origin to the point y_2, η_2 by the following change of coordinates:

$$x = y - y_2 = y - A^{-1}b(\rho - c'A^{-1}b)^{-1}k_0$$

$$\theta = \eta - \eta_2 = \eta - (\rho - c'A^{-1}b)^{-1}k_0.$$

Thus the kinetic equations are

$$\dot{x} = Ax - b\theta$$

$$\dot{\theta} = k(\theta + \eta_2)$$

$$k = c'x - \rho\theta$$

where $\theta + \eta_2 = \eta > 0$.

Now $\sigma = \log[(\theta + \eta_2)/\eta_2]$ is well defined since the argument of log is always positive and θ, σ vanish together. Thus the above equations can be written

$$\dot{x} = Ax - b\eta_2(e^{\sigma} - 1)$$

$$\dot{\sigma} = c'x - \rho\eta_2(e^{\sigma} - 1)$$

which is the standard form for indirect control with $\phi(\sigma) = \eta_2(e^{\sigma} - 1)$. Hence all the theory developed in the text may be applied to this important physical problem.

143

BIBLIOGRAPHY

André, J., and Seibert, P.
[1] Über stückweise lineare Differentialgleichungen die bei Regelungsproblemen auftreten. I. *Arch. Math.* **7**, pp. 148–156 (1956).
[2] Automatic and remote control. *Proc. 1st Internat. Congr. Internat. Federation Automat. Control, Moscow, USSR, 1960* **2**, pp. 919–922 (1961). Butterworths, London.
Aizerman, M. A.
[1] On a problem on the stability of dynamical systems in the large. *Uspehi Mat. Nauk* **4** (1949).
Aizerman, M. A., and Gantmacher, F. R.
[1] Absolute stability of control systems. Russian (1963). English transl. Holden-Day, San Francisco, 1963.
Auslander, J., and Seibert, P.
[1] Prolongations and generalized Liapunov functions. *In* "International Symposium on Nonlinear Differential Equations and Nonlinear Mechanics" (J. F. LaSalle and S. Lefschetz, eds.), pp. 454–462. Academic Press, New York, 1963.
Barbashin, E. A., and Krassovskii, N. N.
[1] On the existence of a Liapunov function in the case of asymptotic stability in the large. *Prikl. Mat. Meh.* **18**, pp. 345–350 (1954).
Bellman, R.
[1] "Introduction to Matrix Analysis." McGraw-Hill, New York, 1960.
A very interesting and lively presentation of the subject. Contains many interesting problems.
Bushaw, D. W.
[1] Optimal discontinuous forcing terms (Princeton thesis, 1953). *In* "Contributions to the Theory of Nonlinear Oscillations" (S. Lefschetz, ed.), **4** (Ann. of Math. Studies No. 41), pp. 29–52. Princeton Univ. Press, Princeton, New Jersey, 1958.

144

Doetsch, G.
[1] "Theorie und Anwendung der Laplace-Transformation." Dover, New York, 1943.
A standard work on Laplace transformations.

Filippov, A. F.
[1] Application of the theory of differential equations with discontinuous right hand sides to nonlinear problems in automatic control. *Proc. 1st Internat. Congr. Internat. Federation Automat. Control, Moscow, USSR, 1960* **1**, pp. 1098–1100 (1960). Butterworths, London.

Gantmacher, F. R.
[1] "The Theory of Matrices," 2 vols. Chelsea, New York, 1959 (Russian, English transl.). Classical and very complete book on matrices, also underscoring relations with vectors and applications to differential equations.

Kalman, R. E.
[1] Canonical structure of linear dynamical systems. *Proc. Nat. Acad. Sci. U.S.A.* **48**, pp. 596–600 (1962).
[2] Liapunov functions for the problem of Lurie in automatic controls. *Proc. Nat. Acad. Sci. U.S.A.* **49**, pp. 201–205 (1963).
A highly important and striking paper.

Kalman, R. E., Ho, Y. C., and Narendra, K. S.
[1] Controllability of linear dynamical systems. *Contrib. Differential Equations* **1**, pp. 189–213 (1963).
A noteworthy paper.

LaSalle, J. P.
[1] Complete stability of a nonlinear control system. *Proc. Nat. Acad. Sci. U.S.A.* **48**, pp. 600–603 (1962).
Noteworthy contribution to our topic.
[2] Stability and control. *SIAM J. Control*, **1**, pp. 3–15 (1963).
Excellent introduction and interesting applications.
[3] The time optimal control problem. *In* "Contributions to the Nonlinear Theory of Oscillations" (S. Lefschetz, ed.), **5**, (Ann. of Math. Studies No. 45), pp. 1–24, Princeton Univ. Press, Princeton, New Jersey, 1960.

LaSalle, J. F., and Lefschetz, S.
[1] "Stability by Liapunov's Direct Method with Applications." Academic Press, New York, 1961.
Elementary introduction to Liapunov's stability theory with many applications among others to control theory.

Lefschetz, S.
[1] "Differential Equations: Geometric Theory," 2nd ed. Wiley (Interscience), New York, 1963.
Contains all the general differential equation theory required for reading the present monograph.
[2] Controls: an application of the direct method of Liapunov. *Bol. Soc. Mat. Mexicana*, **5**, pp. 139–143 (1960).
[3] Some mathematical considerations of nonlinear automatic controls. *Contrib. Differential Equations* **1**, pp. 1–28 (1963).

145

BIBLIOGRAPHY

Letov, A. M.
[1] "Stability of Nonlinear Controls," 1st ed. Princeton Univ. Press, Princeton, New
Jersey, 1961; 2nd ed., 1963 (Russian, English transl.).
One of the early books on nonlinear control theory with many practical examples.
Liapunov, A. M.
[1] "Problème général de la stabilité du mouvement" (Ann. of Math. Studies No. 17).
Princeton Univ. Press, Princeton, New Jersey, 1947.
A classical paper. Very rich and varied material. *Required reading* for anyone who
wishes to study differential equations in *depth*.
[2] "Complete Works," II (Russian).
Lurie, A. I.
[1] "On Some Nonlinear Problems in the Theory of Automatic Control." H. M.
Stationery Office, London, 1951 (Russian, English transl.).
The most important early paper on nonlinear control theory.
Malkin, I. G.
[1] "Theory of Stability of Motion," 1952 (Russian. English transl. by Atomic Energy
Commission, Washington, D.C.).
Very rich material and well written; rather poor translation.
Minorsky, N.
[1] Directional stability of automatically steering bodies. *J. Soc. of Naval Engrs.* (May
1922).
Morozan, T.
[1] Remarques sur une note de Yacubovich. *Compt. Rend.* **254**, pp. 1127–1129 (1962).
Niemickii, V. V., and Stepanov, V. V.
[1] "Qualitative Theory of Differential Equations" (Math. Ser. Princeton, No. 22).
English version. Princeton Univ. Press, Princeton, New Jersey, 1960.
Perhaps the best treatise on modern differential equations. Exceptionally rich content.
Pliss, V. A.
[1] Certain problems in the theory of stability of motion in the large. *Izdatelstvo Lenin-
gradskovo Univ.* (1958) (Russian).
Popov, V. M.
[1] Relaxing the sufficiency conditions for absolute stability. *Avtomat. i Telemeh.* **19**,
pp. 1–7 (1958) (English transl.).
[2] Absolute stability of nonlinear systems of automatic control. *Avtomat. i Telemeh.*
22, pp. 961–979 (1961).
This outstanding and most original paper has marked a date in the development of
our subject. Chapt. VII deals exclusively with it.
[3] On a certain critical case in absolute stability. *Avtomat. i Telemeh.* **23**, pp. 4–24
(1962).
[4] Nouveaux criteriums de stabilité pour les systèmes automatiques non-linéaires.
Rev. Électrotech. Énergét. Acad. R. P. Romîne **5**, pp. 73–88 (1960).
Smets, H. B.
[1] Stability in the large of heterogeneous power reactors. *Bull. Acad. Roy. Belgique Cl. Sci.*
47, pp. 382–405 (1961).

Titchmarsh, E. C.
[1] "Introduction to the Theory of Fourier Integrals." Oxford Univ. Press (Clarendon), London and New York, 1937.
A standard work on Fourier integrals.

Yacubovich, V. A.
[1] On the stability in the large of the undisturbed motion for the equations of indirect automatic control (Russian). *Vestnik Leningrad. Univ.* p. 19 (1957).
[2] On nonlinear differential equations of systems of automatic control with a single control element. *Vestnik Leningrad. Univ.* pp. 120–153 (1960).
[3] Solution of certain matrix inequalities occurring in the theory of automatic controls. *Dokl. Akad. Nauk SSSR* **143**, pp. 1304–1307 (1962).
A very important paper with many original results.
[4] Absolute stability of nonlinear control systems in the critical cases. *Avtomat. i Telemeh.* **24**(I), pp. 293–303 and (II), pp. 717–731 (1963).

Yoshizawa, T.
[1] Liapunov's function and boundedness of solutions. *Funkcial. Ekvac.* **2**, pp. 95–142 (1959).

Zubov, V. I.
[1] "The Methods of A. M. Liapunov and their Applications." Leningrad, 1957.

INDEX